TRAINING WITH

MISS ABERNATHY

TRAINING WITH
MISS ABERNATHY

---

*a workbook for
erotic slaves
and their owners*

Christina Abernathy

greenery press

Cover photograph of Sybil by C. Owen Johnson, Studio Imago.

Published in the United States by Greenery Press, 3403 Piedmont Ave. #301, Oakland, CA 94611, www.greenerypress.com.

ISBN 1-890159-07-7.

Contents

to Ian Philips
dominus urbanus et rarus

INTRODUCTION

Gentle Reader...

Allow me to be the first to welcome you to Miss Abernathy's Academy. Whether you are an old friend or are investigating your interest in consensual dominance and submission for the first time, I hope you will find something of value between the covers of this modest volume.

Please take a moment to read this introduction before proceeding, as it will give you the necessary background to make the most of your time with us.

For Whom Is This Book Intended?

I have designed this program so that it can be used equally well by several different groups of people. First, trainers of erotic slaves can use the book as the basis for a comprehensive program lasting from three to twelve months or longer. Those who already own a slave but are looking for some new ideas or want to direct the slave to a new level of expertise or specialization will also find the book of use. Finally, I envision the possibility that submissives who are not currently in service, but would like to be, will use this book as a self-directed training program, following their own talents and interests. Since there seem to be relatively few experienced trainers, and many willing and able submissives, I have generally addressed the text directly to the submissive.*

---

* *Submissives who are interested in a correspondence course based on the material in this book should see page 143.*

What Is Slave Training?

For our purposes here, slave training is to be understood as the process by which a person gains the necessary skills and attitudes to willingly serve another person. During this process, the trainee may be properly called a submissive, by which we mean a person who knowingly and willingly gives control of certain parts of his or her life over to another person or persons; we may also refer to such a person as a slave-in-training. A submissive nature may be an inborn quality or a set of learned behaviors – opinions vary on this point – but observation shows that submissives are at their happiest and most fulfilled when allowed to express their submissive desires. One way of expressing submission is through specific acts of service performed for the benefit or pleasure of a dominant. In performing these acts of devotion for another, submissives also serve their own deepest desires and highest purpose. In short, service is their vocation. Therefore, we sometimes refer to them as "service-oriented submissives."

As we shall see, this service may take many forms, from simple acts of obedience to complex roles involving considerable intelligence, skill, and dedication. As you work through this program, you will learn about the types of service for which you are best suited and which you most enjoy. Dominants, for their part, derive deep satisfaction from ordering another's life, and nothing brings them more pleasure than seeing a task performed with skill, love, and devotion. Whether the job is as simple as washing the dishes and making the bed or as complex as organizing a home office or cooking a gourmet meal, the thrill the dominant experiences is directly proportional to the submissive's effort and dedication.

Consequently, you will find that this program focuses at least as much on developing the correct attitudes as it does on attaining certain skills. No matter how technically correct the execution of a task may be, without the inner sense of earnest dedication a submissive brings to the work, the result is worthless.

Why This Book?

Some readers may already be familiar with my first book, *Miss Abernathy's Concise Slave Training Manual*. In it, I set out my personal theories of erotic slave training. As the title implies, the Manual was designed as a guide for trainers. It focused on ethics and etiquette as much as on concrete suggestions for training activities, as I deem these considerations of equal importance. In short, the Manual was the theory; this book is the practice.

Dominant/submissive (D/S) culture is, on the whole, under-represented in the field of BDSM* non-fiction. In addition, most of the available material focuses on a specific gender or sexual orientation; this book, in contrast, is pansexual in its range.

Miss Abernathy firmly believes that the time has come for us to view slavehood as a vocation that requires not just desire, but dedication. I hope that, by giving the wider BDSM community more information about the intricacies of slave training and psychology, I can help increase the respect of this community for submissives and their trainers.

How to Use This Book

As I have already suggested, this program can be used by trainers, owners, and unaffiliated submissives alike. I strongly encourage all readers to work through the "Preliminaries" section (trainers will find the material for a slave interview here) and at very least review the information presented in the "Basic Training" section. The "Household Management" section will be of use to those beginning domestic service, but as it is also a prerequisite for the most of the material presented in "Area Studies," it has been given under a separate heading.

After completing the first three sections, the slave-in-training may wish to proceed to the more specialized Area Studies that reflect his or her interests and talents as well as the dominant's service needs. Despite a higher degree of specialization at this point in the training process, readers will find some overlaps. Related lessons have been cross-referenced for your convenience.

Even if you have your heart set on being a sex slave or a lady's maid, don't neglect your training in other areas. Diversified training will only

---

* BDSM is a catch-all acronym for the related practices of "bondage and discipline" (B/D), "dominance and submission" (D/S) and "sadomasochism" (S/M).

increase your value to the dominant, and you may discover with pleasure a new area of interest or talent.

The course of training is designed to take approximately one week per lesson, although of course it is acceptable to move more slowly. I must caution beginners (particularly those working without the benefit of a trainer) from moving much *more* quickly, as it is important to let your emotions and body catch up with your mind. If you encounter a difficulty, it is always appropriate to slow down or even to set the work aside for a time until you feel better able to take it up again. Remember that slave training in its most intense form involves nothing less than a remaking of one's life priorities. It is not a process that can be rushed.

Who Is Miss Abernathy?

Miss Abernathy notes with gratitude the interest expressed in certain quarters about her person. Let it be known, then, that Miss Abernathy is a dominant persona of an experienced BDSM practitioner living in the San Francisco Bay Area. My education and travels have left their mark on me in the form of an insatiable curiosity about human nature, while my background in teaching has given me a taste for the joys of helping others expand their capacities. Within the D/S world, I have had the privilege to train under several notable dominants, in whose debt I shall forever stand. Since that time, I have had the equal privilege of training a number of talented and dedicated submissives. In addition, the local BDSM community has afforded me an unparalleled opportunity to observe and participate in an ever-changing discussion of BDSM theory and practice. I have also been in the unusual position to observe both the men's and women's leather communities, as well as the pansexual and transgender ones.

I hope that my experience in and love of these erotic arts will only serve to benefit you, gentle reader, as you undertake this exciting adventure.

Yours most truly,

Christina Abernathy (Miss)

I. PRELIMINARIES

In these first weeks, you will be exploring your ideas about submission, learning about the different kinds of slaves, examining your strengths and weaknesses, assessing the risks in undertaking this training, and looking at your expectations of the coming weeks. If you are working with a trainer, you will be asked to share your thoughts and feelings about slavehood in a verbal slave interview*. The written exercises in this section should help you clarify your own ideas; they may also form part of the interview process itself. If you are studying independently, please give yourself sufficient time to complete the exercises. Also, you may wish to consult the opening pages of *Miss Abernathy's Concise Slave Training Manual* (hereafter simply the Manual) if you have any questions about terminology or the concept of consent in D/S relationships.

Lesson 1. What Is a Slave?

In this first lesson, you will be exploring your ideas about slavehood.

Exercise** : Take three slow, deep breaths and clear your mind. Jot down 20 words, phrases, images, or associations that come to mind when you hear the word "slave." Give yourself no more than two minutes to complete this exercise. Do not think; write.

---

* See Manual, pp. 8-10, for more details on conducting a slave interview.

** Please do not allow doubts about your literary talents, spelling skills, or penmanship to deter you from completing the written exercises. Their value lies chiefly in their use as a tool for uncovering your thoughts, emotions, and insights, none of which need to be spelled correctly to be valid.

Now, look at your list. Surprised? Even if you have very positive ideas about D/S and your submissive feelings, you may find that your subconscious holds some unpleasant associations with the concept. It is not unusual for the mind to toss up images of brutality, nonconsensual violence, and painful socio-historical models. These images are the source of an uneasiness that you may feel about D/S. You are not sick or perverted. Why? Because you have control over your choices. You rule your own desires, and one of the options you have is to turn control of those desires over to another person. You have the inalienable right to consent. (You also have the equally inalienable right not to.)

Activity: On an index card or other piece of paper, write an affirmation of your right to consent. If you are not familiar or comfortable with the process of composing affirmations, you can use one of these:

• I have the unalienable right to consent.

• I control my own destiny.

• I choose to live a life of right action in service.

Place this sign someplace where you'll see it several times a day, such as a desk drawer, or your bathroom mirror, or the refrigerator door.

You may find affirmations "hokey" or "too New Age." You are allowed to find them silly. You are also allowed to give them a try, with no obligations.

Suggested Reading*: Sacred Moments: Daily Meditations on the Virtues by Linda Kavelin Popov.

Lesson 2. What Kind of a Slave Am I?

The best slaves are versatile people. They are able to rise to the challenge of a new task with grace. Still, most slaves – like other people –

---

* As part of this training program, I suggest books and other resources that I believe to be of use to slaves-in-training. Do not feel compelled to purchase all or even most of them: You will find them just as easily at your local public library. If you find them of more enduring value, then by all means, obtain a copy for your personal collection. A bibliography can be found in the back of this book.

possess certain talents that they do well to cultivate. Likewise, they may have a burning interest in one aspect or another of slavehood, while other facets leave them cold. While Miss Abernathy would like to encourage her readers not to limit themselves too early, it may be helpful for you to look at your own ideas and preferences regarding slavehood.

Exercise: Imagine you are a live-in slave, serving your ideal dominant. What would your life be like? Choose the answer that most closely fits your dream.

1. At 6 a.m. I am suddenly awakened by...
a. Mistress's bell.
b. Mistress's foot.
c. the alarm clock.
d. the wake-up call.

2. It's time to get dressed. I put on...
a. my uniform.
b. nothing.
c. an apron.
d. a suit.

3. It's a busy day. I spend the morning...
a. mending Master's riding breeches.
b. pleasuring Master.
c. cleaning the hall closet.
d. attending Master as he tours the city.

4. Time for lunch! I eat...
a. in the sitting room.
b. off Mistress's boot.
c. whenever I get a minute.
d. in a nice little café Mistress likes.

5. The best thing about being a slave is...
a. being close to Master.
b. the sex.
c. feeling useful.

d. experiencing new things.

6. My strong point is...
a. my knowledge of fashion.
b. my sex appeal.
c. my organizational skills.
d. my people skills.

7. The hardest part of being a slave is...
a. finding time to keep myself looking good.
b. getting my intellectual needs met.
c. the details, all the little details.
d. being on show all the time.

8. After dinner...
a. Master reads the paper while I polish his shoes.
b. we retire to the boudoir.
c. I do the dishes.
d. we're off to the theater with the Billings-Joneses.

9. Time for bed. I must...
a. lay out Mistress's outfit for tomorrow.
b. make myself available in case Mistress wants a massage.
c. review tomorrow's menu.
d. get some sleep after pleasuring Mistress. I've got to look my best.

10. I dream about...
a. being allowed to accompany Master on a drive.
b. the day Master lets me masturbate for him.
c. a nice long bubble bath and an intimate dinner out with Master.
d. just staying home one weekend and relaxing.

Now, count the number of times you answered (a), (b), (c), or (d). Does any one letter predominate? If so, you may have a natural specialty, as explained below. If your answers fall consistently into two categories, you may be attracted to two related or complementary roles. If your answers are varied, you may be best suited for more general service, or you may still discover another specialty not covered here. Finally, if you notice that you never chose a specific letter, you may feel less enthusiastic about a particular type of service. It is still to your benefit to learn something about that specialty so that your training will be well-rounded.

If you chose mostly (a) answers, you may be a good body servant (lady's maid or valet). You value intimacy with the dominant above all else. You are aware of the importance of your physical appearance, and you like to help others look their best. You like personal attention from the dominant and are proud of any trust s/he places in you. You are most comfortable serving at home, although you enjoy it when guests come to visit because it gives you a chance to display your pretty manners. If you also had a number of (b) answers, you may also enjoy sexual service or Victorian scenarios. If you answered (c) to several questions, you might be a good all-around housekeeper, especially in a small home. If you answered (d) to some questions, you might like to travel with the dominant as a personal secretary or escort.

If you chose mostly (b) answers, you are probably most interested in being a sex slave. You are a highly sexual person with considerable stamina, and you pride yourself on your sexual technique. While most slaves enjoy some sexual attention, the erotic side of slavehood is your main focus. You may be willing to perform some domestic service tasks, especially if you are rewarded with the privilege of pleasuring the dominant. If you had some (a) answers, you might consider learning about massage or makeup application to complement your sexual skills. If you had some (c) answers, you may want to include more household management as part of your training. If you had a number of (d) answers, you may want to focus on your conversation skills to become an escort.

If you chose mostly (c) answers, you are best suited to be a housekeeper and/or cook. You are very organized and have considerable household management skills. You are comfortable dealing with visitors and shopping for the household's needs, but you're just as happy behind the scenes. You don't need very much personal attention and are a self-starter. You derive the greatest satisfaction from attending to the dominant's needs in a quiet, unobtrusive way. If you had some (a) answers, you may want to be closer to the dominant and help with some personal care. If you had some (b) answers, you may fantasize about being used sexually while in the middle of some other task. If you had some (d) answers, you may also have the makings of an excellent personal secretary.

If you chose mostly (d) answers, you want to be an escort. You have an attractive personality and excellent communication skills. You enjoy meeting new people and serving in public. You don't mind if some people think you're the dominant's lover; the two of you know the truth about your relationship. Besides, you're very discreet. If you also had some (a) answers, you may enjoy a more formal role, at least at home or in private. A few (b) answers indicate that you would enjoy attending the dominant at BDSM functions and joining in the fun yourself. If you have some (c) answers, you'd be an excellent butler or personal secretary.

Lesson 3. Assessing Strengths and Weaknesses

When you serve another, you are making a gift of yourself to that person. Your value as a slave – beyond the basic intrinsic value of your humanity – relates directly to the skills and attitudes you bring to the relationship.

For a dominant, much of the joy in owning a slave is in the training, so do not think that you will be rejected if you don't know everything right at the start. At its best, service is a lifelong vocation, and you will never stop learning.

Every journey begins somewhere. In this lesson, you'll be looking at the skills you already have – and those you don't – as a way of planning your itinerary for the weeks to come.

Exercise: List five things you do very well: cook, type, repair cars, give massages, listen, perform oral sex on men...

List five things you don't know how to do, but would like to learn: speak French, decorate cakes, do your own taxes, skydive...

List five things you are embarrassed about not being able to do well: draw, eat with chopsticks, enjoy foreign films...

List five things you love to do but would never admit to in public: watch professional wrestling, masturbate, eat pork rinds...

Activity: In the next week, choose one of the items from the second list – things you'd like to learn – and research how you might begin to learn it. Is there a class you could take? A book you could read? A friend you could ask for help? Begin the journey this week.

Lesson 4. Responsibilities of a Slave-in-Training

One of the most important responsibilities of a slave-in-training is communication. You will be required not only to communicate about everyday things and to report on your activities, but you will also be expected to speak frankly about your inner life.

If you haven't spent much time thinking about your own life's path, you may find it uncomfortable to "confess" your dreams and feelings to another person. In fact, many people cannot, without prompting, name the emotions that they are experiencing at any given moment. It is vital that a slave develop a self-reflective impulse: the habit of examining him- or herself on a regular basis so as to be able to describe accurately and unselfconsciously his or her own state of mind.

The following exercise is designed to help you make the first steps in developing this healthful habit. It is important to keep your hand moving across the page as you answer these questions. Write whatever first comes to mind; your answers are not carved in stone, but are the fluid bubblings of your unconscious mind. You may wish to analyze your answers later, but for now, simply write.

Exercise: Complete the following sentences.

I imagine myself as a slave being able to...

As a slave, I wouldn't be allowed to...

The idea that those things would be forbidden makes me feel...

Just once in my life, I'd like to...

I definitely would not want to...

In my sexiest private fantasy, I...

I have a secret fetish for...

Being in a collar would make me feel...

If I were forbidden to have an orgasm for a whole week, I'd...

When I masturbate, I often think about...

I'd like to learn how to...

Serving my Master or Mistress in public would make me feel...

My most erotic memory is...

I first learned about erotic slavehood when...

My favorite book is...

My favorite movie is...

In my free time, I most often...

The thing I find most attractive in other people is...

My highest priority in life is...

Sometimes I doubt I'll ever be able to...

I think most of my romantic involvements have been...

In the past, I was ashamed of...

I feel I've come to terms with...

If there's one negative emotion I can't handle, it's...

When a person raises their voice to me, I...

The three things I associate with silence are...

If pressed, I'd identify myself as...

The biggest influence on my erotic life has been...

I'd describe my spiritual life as...

I believe strongly that...

I'd fight for my right to...

I've only ever wanted to...

Suggested Reading: If you find it difficult to name your feelings, you may find The Book of Qualities *by J. Ruth Gendler enlightening.*

Lesson 5. Assessing Risk: Your Relationships, Work, and Health

All changes involve risk. Risk-taking is an integral part of growth and learning. As you work on the following exercise, you will assess the risks you may take by entering into a slave training program.

Often when we start to follow our dreams, we experience conflict with people around us. This conflict can be the result of envy, fear, confusion, or a simple lack of information. In order to make an informed decision – that is, to give your consent to beginning a training program – you need to look carefully at your relationships and the effect that your new work may have on them. This exercise may seem daunting, especially if your friends are not knowledgeable about D/S or have expressed concerns about your involvement with it. By facing obstacles head-on, you stand the best chance of overcoming them.

The same holds true for your work life and your health. Training as a slave will present you with new and exciting challenges. It is important for you to take a careful look at your limitations, so that you can communicate them to your trainer. There is no shame in having limits, only in disregarding them.

Relationships

Exercise: Rate your responses to the following statements. Use a scale of 1-10 where 1 means "never" or "absolutely not" and 10 means "always" or "most definitely."

I am most comfortable when in a monogamous relationship.

I enjoy feeling helpless or "out of control" sometimes.

I am attracted to members of my own gender.*

I am uncomfortable if I don't know what my partner is thinking.

My family knows about my interest in D/S and they're all right with it.**

My friends know about my interest in D/S and they're supportive of my choices.

If my neighbors found out about my interest in D/S, it wouldn't bother them in the least.

My therapist is comfortable discussing my interest in D/S and seems to know something about consensual BDSM.†

Work

Exercise: Describe your current job (or other sources of income). In what ways do you imagine slavehood might affect your work? If your employer or co-workers found out about your interest in D/S, what would be the most likely outcome?

If you quit your job today, where would you stand financially?

Suggested Reading: Much BDSM erotica might lead you to believe that only those of independent means can be dominants and that all submissives

---

* If your response to this statement was, "I'd answer if I knew what gender I was!" then you may enjoy Kate Bornstein's My Gender Workbook.

** While Miss Abernathy acknowledges that opinions on child-rearing vary greatly, she feels compelled to express her strong conviction that it is inappropriate – and potentially harmful – to involve children in adult sexual relationships. It is inapproriate to divulge the details of your private life to any children in your care. It is also important to assess how any responsibilities you might take on as a slave-in-training would affect your ability to care for children, and make your decisions accordingly.

† Access http://www.bannon.com/kap/ for list of therapists and other professionals who are knowledgeable about BDSM.

should be ready to drop their careers, living spaces, and friends at a moment's notice in order to serve. As a reality check, I suggest you read the opening chapters of two well-known D/S classics and compare how the authors handle the issue of money. First read John Preston's <u>Mr. Benson,</u> and then turn to <u>The Slave</u> by Sara Adamson (Laura Antoniou). Which book seems more realistic to you?

Health

Activity: Ask your doctor for a copy of your medical history for your own files. Make a list of all the medications (including over-the-counter drugs, medicinal herbs, vitamins, and nutritional supplements) that you use. Date the list, and add this to your medical history file. Be sure to update the list as needed.

Activity: If you have not had a thorough general physical for more than three years, schedule an appointment with your doctor for one. This is especially important if you have any unusual health problems.

Exercise: Answer the following questions in detail and be scrupulously honest. A positive answer to any of these questions does *not* disqualify someone for service. In fact, those who have weathered adversity are often stronger and enjoy greater self-knowledge than their "more fortunate" peers, making them especially well-prepared for training. It is vital, in any case, that your trainer have this information to help maintain your personal safety. If you are working without a trainer, consider the implications of your answers. Would a lifestyle change or professional assistance make it easier for you to serve?

Do you have any allergies?

Do you have any dietary restrictions? Are you vegetarian or vegan?

Do you have any chronic illnesses or injuries that trouble you? What sort of treatment do you use?

Do you wear eyeglasses or contact lens? A hearing aid?

Do you use any drugs (including alcohol or tobacco) recreationally? What and how often?

Are you currently struggling with an addiction?

Are you aware of any body image issues that trouble you?

Are you clean and/or sober? For how long?

Are you in recovery from an addiction other than alcohol or drugs? For how long?

Did you suffer any abuse (physical, verbal, psychological, sexual, spiritual...) as a child?

Have you suffered such abuse as an adult?

How have you learned to heal these wounds?

If you have a history of abuse, can you identify any "triggers" (words, sounds, objects, situations) that might cause you trauma now?

Do you have any history of abusing others? If so, what steps have you taken to change this pattern?

Suggested Reading: The Body Image Workbook, by Thomas F. Cash. Self-Esteem Comes in All Sizes, by Carol A. Johnson.

Resources: Many major cities now have recovery groups for BDSM practitioners. Call your local AA or NA Central Office for details.

Lesson 6. Expectations: the Training Contract

The purpose of a training contract is to spell out, in detail, the respective responsibilities of the trainer and the trainee. It may be useful for you to think of the training contract in terms of an "at-will" employment agreement. Such an agreement states that both employer and employee reserve the right to cancel the agreement at will and explains the process for doing so. (This generally includes the requirement that either party give written notice the other in the event that the agreement is to be dissolved.) Further, it specifies the starting date of employment, a job description, salary and any benefits that the employer will provide, such as health insurance, transit costs, or uniforms.

If you are working with a trainer, no doubt he or she will have a standard contract for you to examine. If you believe that you will be unable to fulfill any clause of the contract or do not wish to do so, it is your right – indeed, your obligation – to ask for further negotiation until you can reach a mutually agreeable compromise.

All training contracts should include the following:
- the starting date and ending dates of the contract;
- the specific responsibilities of both parties, including financial ones;
- safewords or some other signal for a "time-out";
- physical and psychological limitations of the parties;
- a discussion of punishment (what forms it may take, when it will be used...);
- any specific rituals or formulas or titles that play a role in the fulfillment of the contract;
- circumstances under which the contract will become null and void;
- the goal of the contract. (This may be as simple as "the training of a slave to our mutual satisfaction" or a list of skills to be acquired; it may also include a philosophical statement on the nature of slavehood as the trainer understands it.)

How can a slave working independently draw up a contract? Since a training contract is an agreement between two (or more) people, clearly an individual cannot be subject to one. Miss Abernathy instead suggests that such a submissive write a Statement of Purpose in which he or she makes a personal commitment to work through the training program. Since you are essentially both trainer and trainee, be sure to specify the responsibilities you have toward yourself: excellent self-care, sufficient food, sleep, exercise, and recreation, and most of all, compassion.

Suggested Reading: Manual, pp. 57-64.

II. Basic Training

Lesson 7. Obedience I : First Steps toward Mindfulness

If you were to ask one hundred submissives for a definition of "obedience," ninety-five of them would tell you that means doing as you're told or following orders. In the strict sense, they would be correct.

But what if you received the following order: "Tell me what you are feeling right now!" Would you be able to answer clearly and accurately?

And what about the situations in which no verbal command is issued? Perhaps you are faced with a difficult choice and the dominant is not present to guide you. How can you act in the spirit of obedience if the "letter of the law" is missing?

Exercise: After you finish reading the instructions for this exercise, but without looking around you first, close your eyes. Now name three things in the room that are behind you, to your right, to your left, and in front of you.

This exercise will have given you some insight into your skills of observation. The next time you are in an unfamiliar environment, try the exercise again. Does being in a new place change your observations?

Now you will learn a technique to help you observe not only your physical surroundings, but also yourself.

Activity: Sit comfortably with your spine straight. You may choose to sit in a chair or cross-legged on the floor, as long as you can maintain the position for at least 20 minutes. Do not lie down, as this posture encourages drowsiness.

Now, close your eyes, and draw your attention to your breath. Observe how the breath enters your nostrils as you inhale and exits as you exhale. Focus your awareness on the point where the breath enters and exits. If thoughts or feelings surface – and they will – simply return your attention to your breath. Do not judge or follow your thoughts; simply return to the breath. Count 10 full breaths (in and out). When you are finished, slowly become aware of your surroundings. When you are ready, open your eyes.

The purpose of this meditation is to help you quiet your mind and to be able to observe the flow of thoughts that arise as you do so. The content of the thoughts is irrelevant. What is important is the insight that the mind is in constant motion, and that it is very difficult to stop or control that motion. We also observe that as thoughts arise, so also do they pass.

Try this meditation every day for at least one week; you may choose to make it a regular part of your training. At first you may only be able to count a single breath before thoughts and feelings come crowding in. This is normal. If you persist – just letting the thoughts pass by like boats on a stream – you will be able to distance yourself from your thoughts and feelings. This distance will allow you the space to name and describe your thoughts and feelings without getting caught up in them.

Suggested Reading: Any book or tape by Fr. Thomas Keating or Thich Nhat Hanh. You need not be Catholic or Buddhist to appreciate the universality of the meditation techniques they teach.

Along with awareness of your inner workings, it is important to cultivate awareness of your physical self. Most submissives find it very difficult to hold their bodies still for any length of time, but this is a vital skill for a slave.

Activity: For this activity, you will need a watch with an unobtrusive alarm function, ideally one that emits a single beep. (You can also use a small alarm clock or timer, as long as the alarm isn't too loud and doesn't beep continuously until you turn it off.) You will be carrying this alarm with you through your day.

Set the alarm to sound at 11 minutes past the hour. When the alarm sounds, bring your attention to your physical posture: Where are your hands? Are your legs crossed? Is your back straight? Your jaw tense? Do you feel any pain in your body? Are you moving any part of your body (jiggling your leg, chewing on a pencil)? When you've assessed your physical state, you may want to take a moment to relax any tension that you've discovered. Now, reset the alarm for the next hour.

Activity: Do you remember the card game Memory? In it, a special deck of cards (or two complete standard decks) are dealt out face down in even rows. The first player turns over two cards. If they match, the player removes them from the table and takes another turn. If they do not match, the player turns them back over and the other player takes a turn. Whoever makes the most matches, wins.

Try this game alone or with a friend. It will help you to develop better observation skills.

Lesson 8. Obedience II: Awareness of Others

The slave-in-training has to strike a careful balance between self-observation and awareness of others. A slave is often called upon to respond to requests indicated by the slightest hand gesture, the half-smile, the raised eyebrow.

If you live in a crowded city or in an active home, you may have learned to "tune out" the hustle and bustle that surrounds you. In this lesson, you will learn to tune back in to the important messages.

Exercise: Think of someone you've met in the last day or two. Can you give the following information about the person: eye color? height? color of their shirt? approximate age? name? How would you characterize their mood or state of mind at the time you met them?

Now, think of someone you see daily who is not a close friend. This might be the person who sells newspapers on the corner, the counter person at your local coffee shop, the person who asks for change outside your work. Can you answer the same questions about them?

Activity: The next time you go out for dinner, pay attention when the server announces, "My name is So-and-so, and I'll be your server tonight." Then use the server's name when you address him or her. (A variation on this activity is to read the name tags many retail workers wear and address them by name.) Note: Ironically, using a person's name in this context is unusual enough that some people may be taken aback by it. To minimize this effect, try using the name when thanking them or requesting help: "Thank you, Susan." "Excuse me, James, could you please bring me another glass of juice?"

Exercise: How can you tell if a person is angry? Depressed? Excited? List five non-verbal cues for each emotion.

Suggested Reading: How to Read a Person Like a Book by Gerald I. Nierenberg and Henry H. Calero is the classic book on body language. Note that their study focuses on white Americans; people of other cultures and ethnic groups within the United States and abroad may use other cues.

Activity: Go to a busy public place, like an outdoor café or a park. Close your eyes. Using your other senses, locate the person who is physically closest to you. What can you say about that person? Can you identify their gender, age, or ethnicity? What can you say about their voice? Can you smell perfume or some other scent? How heavy is their tread? Based on the information you gather, how would you describe this person? Now open your eyes. How accurate was your assessment?

This activity will teach you three important things: first, to use your senses to their fullest; second, to be aware of the limitations of your senses; and third, to notice the extent to which your assumptions can influence what you perceive and how you interpret sensory input.

Suggested Reading: Developing Creative and Critical Thinking: An Integrated Approach by Robert Boostrom is a textbook that can easily be used outside of the classroom. It will help you sharpen your observation skills and hone your mental abilities.

Lesson 9. Obedience III: Self-Discipline

In Lesson 7, you learned some self-observation skills. In the process, you may have discovered some things about yourself that you'd like to change. Perhaps you found that you slump. Or you chew your nails. Or you chatter when you get nervous.

Not only are these habits inappropriate for a slave, but in dealing with them early on in your training, you will gain the added benefit of developing another vital skill: self-discipline.

Activity: Continue to practice the focusing meditation described in Lesson 7. Meditate for 10 minutes daily, and gradually increase your practice until you are meditating for 20 minutes at a sitting, twice a day.

Exercise: Name five individuals who embody the virtue of self-discipline for you. (They may be public figures or people known to you personally.) What can you learn from them?

Suggested Reading: Read a biography of one of your personal models for self-discipline. Note the challenges that person faced and how he or she overcame them.

Lesson 10. Slave Journal: The Discipline of Self-Disclosure

By now you will have started to develop the skills necessary to name your emotions and needs more clearly. These skills have an outer and an inner component. On the outer side, you will be better able to inform your trainer of any difficulties that arise and will be able to answer probing questions about your current state of mind. On the inner side, you will also be cultivating for yourself the habit of Self-Observation. Increased awareness of your own motivations and thought patterns can be, in and of itself, a source of satisfaction.

The present lesson provides yet another technique for communicating with your trainer and working out your own processes. Starting this week, you will keep a written account of your life in the form of a slave journal.

If you are working with a trainer, you will be turning over your journal to that person at regular intervals for evaluation. The journal is a document of your experience, and as such, nothing in it can be "right" or "wrong" per se. It can be more or less detailed, more or less accurate, more or less honest, but it cannot be more or less correct. The only way you can fail at keeping a slave journal is by not writing in it.

Activity: Buy a special notebook or diary to use as a slave journal. It need not be fancy or expensive, although if a blank bound book is within your means, you may find it lends an aura of gravity to the act of writing. But even if your slave journal is a 99-cent spiral-bound notebook, it is an important facet of your training. You should also make sure that you have a pen (not a pencil) with which you can write easily for half an hour.

What should you write in your journal? Entries need not be long, and they do not even have to relate directly to the training process. What is important is the regularity with which you write and the effort you put into naming your emotions and experiences.

Activity: Review the affirmations exercise in Lesson 1. Use one of the suggested sentences or compose one of your own. Before you begin to write, kneel down (as you are able) for a minute and clear your mind. Visualize yourself speaking openly and honestly with your trainer or Owner whom you trust implicitly. Imagine that person responding firmly, but with deep understanding and care. Now, repeat your chosen affirmation: I devote myself to service. I serve for my benefit and that of others. By serving, I fulfill my highest calling. Then write in your journal. When you have finished, repeat your affirmation quietly to yourself.

Exercise: This exercise is for slaves who wish to use the slave journal as a preliminary tool leading to voice-training. Do not use it until you have been writing regularly for at least one month.

Try writing in your journal without using the capital "I" to refer to yourself. You may want to substitute the lower-case letter "i" at first. Later, you may want to avoid personal pronouns and possessives altogether: *this slave spent the day cleaning Mistress's boots and was content.* This can lead to some interesting challenges: if you cannot say "my Master," what do you say? List three possible solutions to this problem.

Suggested Reading: Written to help creatively blocked artists, Julia Cameron's best-selling book, The Artist's Way, contains some words of wisdom on journaling that those who keep slave journals will no doubt find helpful.

Lesson 11. Voice-Training I: Silence

It may seem ironic, but the first step in voice-training is learning when not to speak. For slaves, this will be most of the time. Slaves, like the children in the old saw, are to be "seen and not heard." For a slave, speech is a privilege, not a right.

If you have been working at the meditation practice suggested in earlier lessons, you are becoming more accustomed to silence. We live in a frightfully noisy world, and it is important for you as a slave-in-training to be able to filter out background distractions and focus on the task at hand. Developing inner silence is one effective technique to accomplish this.

Another is the simple practice of choosing silence.

Exercise: Sit quietly in your home with a pen and paper. For five minutes, just listen, as if you were listening to a piece of music. Then write down everything you can remember hearing.

Activity: At least once during this week, consciously choose silence. If you are accustomed to chatting with co-workers during your lunch break, eat out or go to the park. If you suffer a petty insult on the street, do not respond. If you are tempted to make a cutting remark, stop. Say nothing. Just once. If you usually listen to the radio in the car or watch television in the evening, take a day off. Notice how external silence helps you focus on the internal voices... and eventually, to quiet them as well.

Lesson 12. Voice-Training II: Forms of Address

Whether they realize it or not, most slaves do have a certain level of voice-training. Every time they say "Master," or "Mistress," "Sir," or "Ma'am," they are responding to the spoken or unspoken rules that dictate the way a slave speaks to an Owner or trainer.

Exercise: List all the titles of authority you can think of: Sir, Mistress, Officer, Majesty.... In non-scene life, what dictates when you use such a title? What cues (verbal or non-verbal) tell you to show respect by using a title? Is it possible to be disrespectful while using a formal title? What titles have *you* been called?

Exercise: Select a title that denotes dominance to you, and for one week, address your slave journal entries to that figure of authority. Do you find that your tone changes? Are there things you neglect or choose not to write? Why or why not?

Suggested Reading: Any secretarial handbook will list political, academic, and military forms of address. Familiarize yourself with them. (Note that the form used to address the individual directly sometimes differs from the form used in correspondence or when referring to someone indirectly.)

Lesson 13. Personal Care and Fitness for Slaves

When you spend a great deal of time caring for the needs and desires of others, it is all too easy to forget to care for yourself. How many times have you seen a tired, haggard mother with picture-perfect children? If you don't care properly for yourself, physically as well as psychologically, you'll have precious little to offer a dominant.

So no matter how pretty your manners, how manifold your accomplishments, if you are lacking in matters of personal hygiene, you will not go far as a slave. Slaves cannot afford to be overly fussy in matters of appearance, but they neglect the basics of the toilette at their peril. Remember that your own appearance reflects on your trainer or Owner, so don't forget the following grooming basics:

- Frequent showers or baths with a good, effective soap;
- Clean hair, whatever the style;
- Appropriate use of deodorant/antiperspirant for your body chemistry and activity level;
- Clean, trimmed nails;
- Clean teeth and fresh breath;
- Clean, pressed clothing in good repair.

Exercise: List all of the personal care products you use: soap, shampoo, toothpaste, moisturizer, shaving cream....

Activity: If you use only the most basic grooming aids (soap, shampoo, and toothpaste, say), indulge in some bath oil or a scented soap. If you have more shades of lipstick than the Queen has jewels, try spending a weekend using just the basics.

Activity: Treat yourself to a manicure, pedicure, facial, or massage (or all of these) at a day spa or salon. Alternatively, you can create a spa experience for yourself at home. See *The Wellness Center's Spa at Home* by Kalia Doner and Margaret Doner for tips. Not only will a day of pampering make you feel delicious, you will also learn both how to care for yourself and how to perform some important "body service" tasks as well.

Basic fitness is also important for a slave. This isn't fitness for its own sake, but fitness for the tasks at hand. A light exercise program focusing on flexibility and balance is very helpful for a slave. A brisk daily walk and some simple stretches or yoga postures will do wonders for both your body and your spirit. However, as dominants' needs vary, so do slaves' physical abilities. You don't need to be an Olympic athlete – or for that matter, completely able-bodied – to serve, so don't allow fitness to become an obsession or a cause for self-deprecation.

Activity: Rent or purchase an exercise video that teaches basic stretches or yoga. Establish a simple exercise regime for yourself: a walk around the park, some deep knee bends and shoulder rolls.... If you work at a desk, be sure to get up at least once every thirty minutes to avoid tension and injury.

For further training, see the lessons on shaving and cleansing enemas and douches. For information on body service, see the Lady's Maid & Valet sections in "Area Studies."

Suggested Reading: If you're unfamiliar with men's grooming, read Paisley Goes with Nothing, pp. 101-134, for a concise and witty presentation of the basics. Men's magazines like GQ and Details offer grooming tips as well. In our culture, women are all too often inundated with advice on how to make themselves more attractive, most of it rubbish. Beyond the basics of cleanliness, sufficient sleep, and good posture, forget everything you've read about the wonders of cosmetics. What holds for men, holds for you, with or without Miraculous Anti-Wrinkle Gel.

Lesson 14. Positioning the Body: Waiting and At Rest Postures

Ask experienced slaves what occupies most of their time, and they will tell you, "Waiting." Along with the mental habits of mindfulness, observance, and quiet, slaves must train themselves to wait gracefully. Fidgeting is unbecoming in a slave. Luckily (if you will), modern life affords us all ample opportunity to practice our waiting skills.

Activity: The next time you find yourself waiting – in line at the supermarket, on hold on the telephone – try this simple exercise.

Observe your body and adopt an alert but relaxed posture. If you are standing, try moving your legs apart slightly so that you can balance evenly on both legs, rather than shifting your weight from side to side. Keep your knees slightly bent, not straight.

Now, quiet your mind by breathing slowly and evenly. (If you have been meditating regularly, this process will have become almost second nature.) Allow your eyes to maintain a soft focus on the floor approximately six feet in front of you.

Repeat your chosen affirmation to yourself silently.

One of the most common errors slaves-in-training make is to fidget with their hands. This next activity will help you become aware of your hands.

Activity: Stand with your weight balanced evenly on both feet, remembering to keep your knees bent ever-so-slightly. Allow your arms to hang comfortably at your sides. Consciously tense your hands by balling them into fists, and then release. Your now relaxed hands will naturally form a gently curved "cup" shape. (Pianists will recognize this as the correct hand position for keyboards as well.)

Now sit down on a straight-backed chair and rest your hands palms-down on your thighs. Notice that your hands will form the same "cup" shape. Now turn your hands palms up, Again, they retain the natural shape when relaxed, without stress or strain on the arms or wrists. This is a pretty, receptive posture and should be adopted when sitting or kneeling.

Activity: Stand and hold your arms behind your back with your hands together over the base of your spine. You may have to hold one of your wrists with the other hand. See how long you can maintain this posture without fatigue.

Activity: Kneel on a soft surface (like a rug or folded bath towel). Rest your buttocks on your ankles. (This is sometimes called "kneeling down," as opposed to "kneeling up" with your upper body at a right angle to your lower legs.) Position your hands in the receptive posture described above and lower your head so that your gaze falls on the floor about four feet in front of you. Try to stay in this position for five minutes without moving. (The "waiting" exercise given above may help you.)

Safety Warning: If you have knee problems or feel any pain when kneeling, do not do it. Practice standing instead. Always be sure to inform your trainer if you experience any physical discomfort from a posture.

Suggested Reading: For information on other useful basic postures, see Manual, pp. 15-19.

Lesson 15. Voice Commands and Body Positions

Slaves must be able to respond to verbal commands without hesitation. If you are asked to move, you should do so quickly, but gracefully. Do not run unless specifically commanded to, as it greatly increases the risk of accidents.

If you are working with a trainer, you will be drilled until you can respond to voice commands with ease. If you are working independently, the following activity will help you.

Activity: Using a blank cassette tape and a tape recorder, make a tape that includes the following commands: Come here, go, attend, present, open, down, worship, wait. Wind the tape forward, then speak one of the commands into the recorder. Wind the tape forward again a space, then speak another command. Try to vary the order of the commands as well as the length of time between them. You may also want to give two or more commands in quick succession. When you are finished, you can play the tape (try a Walkman) and assume each position as you hear it. (Please be sure to do some basic stretches before you begin to avoid straining yourself.) Obviously you should only practice at home or in some other private place. (For the "come here" command, approach a specific chair; for "go," face the same chair and exit the room without turning your back on the chair. Practice both walking and crawling.)

Activity: Record a second tape, but this time speak the commands more rapidly, one after the other. Allow approximately three seconds between commands. (Count *one one thousand, two one thousand, three one thousand* silently between commands.) With practice, you will be able to move gracefully from one position to the next. You may find it helpful to practice in front of a mirror. Try the exercise naked as well.

Activity: After you've been working with the command tapes or a while, try videotaping yourself as you assume the various positions. You should work toward smooth, fluid movements without jerks or stops.

Resources: If you are not used to much physical activity, you may want to take a stretching or beginning yoga class. There are many exercise videos available to home use as well; choose one that emphasizes flexibility.

Safety Warning: If you experience pain during these exercises, stop. Be sure to do some simple stretches before you begin to minimize the chances of pulling a muscle.

Lesson 16. Exploring Feelings about Punishment

As we near the end of the Basic Training section, we turn to one of the more troubling topics: punishment. Few people enjoy punishment for its own sake; some find it exciting in the context of erotic role-play. Nevertheless, most slaves will see the importance of some form of discipline as a pedagogical aid.

All punishment need not be corporal: in fact, I have found physical punishment to be among the least effective tools, as it tends to throw the slave into a vat of roiling emotions (many of them shadows of childhood) that make it impossible for the slave to think clearly. Corporal punishment does hold an important place in many people's erotic imaginations, and so maintains its place among the many forms of punishment a trainer or Owner may impose upon a wayward slave.

I do not suggest that punishments per se be imposed slaves until they have completed at least the most basic aspects of training. This is for the simple reason that, unless slaves have been taught what exactly is expected of them, they can't be held accountable if they fail to live up to a trainer's standards. Slaves aren't mind readers after all. Hence the delay in attending to this delicate, albeit important, matter.

Exercise: Choose the answer that most accurately reflects your feelings.

1. You discover that you have made an error in a report that could cause your company to lose a significant amount of business. What do you do?
a. I run off a errata slip to be included with the report, and give it to the person sending out the mailing.
b. I inform my supervisor of the error immediately.
c. I stay late to retype the report.
d. I say nothing and pray the error won't be noticed. But I worry for weeks about the consequences.

2. When I was a child and my parents found out I'd broken a rule, they...
a. my parents? They were too busy to notice anything.
b. wanted to understand why I'd done it.
c. sometimes gave me weird punishments that didn't fit the crime.
d. said nothing, but gave me disappointed looks for days afterward.

3. The most important thing for children is that they...
a. be allowed freedom, but with clear limitations.
b. be encouraged to share their feelings and doubts.
c. be treated fairly.
d. be given lots of attention and love.

4. The hardest punishment for me to take would be...
a. being publicly disgraced.
b. being yelled at.
c. being sent away.
d. being ignored.

5. I think the worst thing a slave can do is...
a. get caught doing something wrong.
b. not communicate with the Owner.

c. not take steps to correct an error.

d. talk back to the Owner.

6. The stupidest punishment I've ever experienced was...

a. being grounded.

b. having to write some dumb sentence about 8 million times.

c. being spanked.

d. being given the silent treatment.

7. It would be easy for me to...

a. listen to a lecture on what I did wrong. At least I'd understand the problem better.

b. confess wrongdoing to the Owner. At least I'd have done the right thing morally.

c. have to re-do a task. At least I'd know how to do it better the next time.

d. deal with being physically punished. At least it's over right away.

8. When I was punished as a child, I mostly felt...

a. angry.

b. embarrassed.

c. dumb.

d. ashamed.

9. In slave training, I think punishment is...

a. a necessary evil.

b. a last resort.

c. one of the ways a slave learns.

d. one of the things I fear most.

And one more question:

10. I am...

a. a happy masochist.

b. open to exploring my masochistic fantasies.

c. not thrilled about the idea of physical punishment.

d. not into the SM side of things at all.

Now, count the number of times you chose (a), (b), (c), and (d) for questions 1-9.

If you chose mostly (a) answers, you tend to be sure of yourself and your abilities. You'll admit to making a mistake if pressed, but you'd rather just quietly cover your tracks and move on. Why rock the boat? is your motto. You may have grown up in a busy household, so you learned to handle crises for yourself. You tend to focus on the end result, not the means. You may have a hard time if you are punished for philosophical or ethical reasons, especially if no obvious harm resulted from your actions.

If you chose mostly (b) answers, you are not often in charge and prefer to have a superior to confer with. You probably have good verbal skills and are considered a "team player." When you make a mistake, the first thing you do is go back over your actions step by step until you uncover the "false move." For you, the process is at least as important as the end result. If you are reprimanded, you want to know what, specifically, you did wrong and how to avoid the same error in the future.

If you chose mostly (c) answers, you tend toward perfectionism. You want to see an error corrected at all costs. You may tend to overemphasize your intellectual side and may respond to punishment by berating yourself. You may judge yourself by unrealistically high standards, and it's hard for you to let someone else judge you, particularly if their standards differ from yours. You value fairness and balance, so you want to see the punishment fit the crime. Consequently, you may find corporal punishment frustrating or degrading.

If you chose mostly (d) answers, you tend to stew over errors you make, but are afraid to admit them, fearing the worst. As a result, your self-esteem suffers. You may have grown up in an authoritarian household, or your parents may have been emotionally distant. You may suffer from fear of abandonment. It is very difficult for you to confess wrong-doing, but you find it cathartic to do so. You crave positive reinforcement and supportive attention. If you are physically punished, you need reassurance that you have not failed totally.

If your answers were evenly divided between several letters, take note of any insights you may have gained from the exercise. What do you most fear about punishment? What childhood memories does it evoke? What, in your view, is the role of punishment in slave training?

You may wonder how question 10 fits into this scheme. Devising punishments for masochists remains a perennial problem for slave trainers. Unlike other submissives, masochistic slaves-in-training rarely derive benefit from corporal punishment, since they experience pleasure in intense sensation.

The solution, of course, is either to punish masochists with a type of sensation they dislike or to avoid corporal punishment altogether.

If you are working independently, this lesson will have served as an exercise in greater self-knowledge. Miss Abernathy cautions you against self-inflicted punishments, as it is all too easy to lose perspective. Instead, note your shortcomings in your slave journal.

Lesson 17. The Collar

The collar is the symbol par excellence of slavehood. It is an outward symbol of your state of servitude and of your Owner's (or trainer's) care for you. Unlike the slave journal, which legally and morally is yours, the collar remains the possession of the Owner and must be surrendered upon demand.

Since it is such a potent sign of a slave's position, the choice of collar is a delicate one. While you, as property, have no direct say in the style of the collar – that is for your trainer or Owner to decide – it may prove useful for you to think, in theoretical terms at least, about the collar as symbol.

Exercise: Write a paragraph describing your dream collar. What kind of material is it made of? Does it lock? Does it include a tag ("This slave owned by...")? Could you wear this collar in non-scene public? Why or why not? How would others respond to seeing you in this collar? What feelings would the collar evoke in you?

Activity: Make a list of five substitutes for the traditional black leather slave collar. Try wearing one of these substitutes for a day. How does it make you feel? Do you find yourself aware of the collar? Of yourself as a slave-in-training?

Safety Warning: Take care that the item you choose does not obstruct your breathing; this is especially important if you want to sleep in the collar or perform hard physical labor or exercise, as your neck may swell.

Activity: Visit a shop that sells slave collars and try some on.

Suggested Reading: Manual, pp. 1-2 and 25-27.

III. HOUSEHOLD MANAGEMENT

It is my assumption that most slaves will be engaged in some form of domestic service. In this day and age, however, it is impossible to make any assumptions about a slave's preparedness for this kind of work, regardless of age or gender. Further, housekeeping standards and needs vary so greatly from person to person, that it is difficult to predict what any one dominant might require of you. Therefore, in this section I have undertaken a thorough discussion – perhaps, for some individuals, a review – of the rudiments of household management.

For the purposes of this section of the book, I will assume that you are the sole servant on hand and that the household in your care is of such size that no other help would be needed. Likewise, I assume that your Owner has turned over all basic household responsibilities to you and takes no active role, beyond the fiscal, in maintaining the household.

I strongly recommend that all slaves-in-training avail themselves of the information herein, even if they have no expectation of becoming house servants. Most dominants are busy people and would be delighted to find a slave who is as competent in the kitchen as in the bedroom. Further, some dominants will assess potential slaves by employing them first as houseboys. If they pass muster and prove trustworthy, they may be invited to receive further training. (This is a common practice among professional dominants.)

Suggested Reading: In addition to the specific volumes mentioned in the lessons themselves, all domestic servants should come to terms with the basics of time management. Despite their cumbersome titles, the following books may prove of assistance: The Complete Idiot's Guide to Managing Your Time by Jeff Davidson, and The Overwhelmed Person's Guide to Time Management by Ronni Eisenberg with Kate Kelly. I also suggest Organizing for the

Creative Person by Dorothy Lehmkuhl and Dolores Cotter, with the caveat that you must consider your Owner's personality type along with your own as you follow the authors' plan. Finally, _Organizing Hints & Tips_ by Cassandra Kent is a gem.

Lesson 18. Housework I: Basic Cleaning

Like most of us in this day and age, dominants are busy people. Professional organizers and cleaning services proliferate in our cities as more and more people have less and less time. Add to this the fact that for many people, cleaning house is about as much fun as a trip to the dentist, and you'll begin to understand why many dominants expect slaves to be competent in housekeeping.

As a slave-in-training, you may surprised to find that cleaning someone else's house is a very different experience from cleaning your own. Instead of grousing, "How little cleaning can I get away with?" you will find yourself enjoying dusting baseboards and yes, doing windows. Why? Because service-oriented submissives derive satisfaction not only from a job well done, but from the very fact of having performed a task for someone whom they love and admire.

Housecleaning

However noble your intentions, though, you may feel overwhelmed when faced with a house in (sometimes desperate) need of cleaning. In this lesson we will be looking at the steps you'll take to develop and execute a thorough cleaning plan. In addition, we'll be looking at some basic laundry techniques. (For more information on clothing care, please see the section on Valets and Lady's Maids in "Area Studies.")

Activity: Read through the following steps quickly, then follow them for the home you wish to clean. This may be, for the time being, your own home, or that of your trainer. If at any time you find yourself feeling overwhelmed, take a moment to focus your mind with the meditation techniques described in the "Basic Training" section. You are not expected to complete all the steps in this activity in one session, nor even in one day, particularly if the home is large or its cleaning has been neglected.

1) Inventory the rooms. In this step, you walk from room to room and make notes on what needs cleaning. You'll want to note any special features of the room – high ceilings, French doors, antique rugs – that need special attention. You may find it helpful to sketch a diagram of the room, marking furniture, fixtures, and other details.

2) Go over your list room by room and see if there is anything you don't already know how to clean. Look up the information in a good reference book (see the suggested reading list for Miss Abernathy's favorites).

3) Break the job into small, manageable tasks. This step is vital to your success. If you think, "I have to clean the entire house this morning," you'll become disheartened and run the risk of spending your time worrying instead of cleaning. If you say, "I have to dust the credenza right now," you'll be better able to approach the task.

4) Gather your tools. Again, you may want to refer to a book if you are unsure of what you'll need. Consider environmentally safe cleansers like vinegar, baking soda, and lemon juice: They are not only more pleasant to use, but you'll save money as well. (See the lesson for Housekeepers for some more ideas on "green" cleaning.) Be sure to wear lined rubber gloves to protect your skin, and if you must use toxic chemicals, read and follow the safety guidelines on the package.

5) Complete each task before moving to the next. (A half-polished silver tea service is no more useful than a completely tarnished one.)

6) Complete each room before moving to the next. It is helpful to start your cleaning to the right of the door you entered by and work clockwise around the room until you are finished.

7) Note down any difficulties you encounter so you can search for alternative cleaning methods. (For example, if you tried to clean a bathtub with a non-abrasive cleanser, but found it didn't cut through the soap film, you will want to try an abrasive cleanser.) When you find a method that works particularly well, record it in a household journal.

8) To help you better plan your time, note how long each task takes. Many will become easier with practice, so don't be dismayed.

9) Finally, draw up a regular schedule for housecleaning. It should include tasks to be done daily, weekly, biweekly, monthly, semi-annually, and annually. For example, beds should be made daily, and sheets changed weekly, but mattresses need be turned only semi-annually. Scheduling will help you distinguish the more important tasks from the less. Most of the suggested books contain schedules that can be adapted to your specific needs.

Suggested Reading: If there is only one reading suggestion you take, let it be this: Cassandra Kent's <u>Household Hints & Tips</u>. This invaluable guide shows you – with the aid of clear illustrations – how to handle everything from basic household cleaning to artificial respiration. Second only to Kent are <u>Speed Cleaning</u> and <u>Spring Cleaning</u> by Jeff Campbell and the Clean Team.

Activity: Hire a professional cleaning service to spring-clean your house. Watch how the cleaners work. (You will want to tell them that you'll be observing them "to pick up some cleaning tips" so they don't feel intimidated.) If hiring a service isn't an option for you, please read the Clean Team books cover to cover.

Activity: Many newspapers have a "household hints" column. Make a point of reading it regularly; clip or jot down any useful tips.

Laundry

Along with housecleaning, most slaves in domestic service will be expected to attend to the household laundry. Whether you have access to a washer and dryer in the house or will be taking the laundry out, there are a few important factors to bear in mind.

1) Sort the laundry by color. Whites should be washed by themselves. Miss Abernathy prefers light and dark colors to be separated as well, rendering approximately three loads.

2) Read the labels on clothing to determine the types of fabrics. Most labels also have laundry instructions.

3) Select the water temperature and wash cycle based on the most delicate item in the load. You should use the hottest water that the fabrics can withstand. In general, whites should be washed in hot water, colors in warm, and any non-colorfast items in cold. All rinses can be in cold water.

4) Do not use too much detergent, especially in industrial washers which often contain the residue of previous users' soap. It is not the suds that clean clothes, but the (often invisible) cleansers and borax in the detergent. In fact, many products contain a sudsing agent only because consumers expect to see suds. These sudsing agents are not only unnecessary but may be harmful to the environment.(For information on treating stains on clothing, consult Cassandra Kent's Household Hints & Tips.)

5) Bleach should be used sparingly, as it is caustic and causes fibers to weaken. Always dilute bleach in water and then add clothes. Do not use liquid bleach on colors; choose a powder specifically designed for use on colors.

6) If you use fabric softener, it should be added to the rinse cycle. (Note that fabric softeners can be irritating to the skin because of the perfumes they contain. If you are doing laundry for a person with allergies or sensitive skin, choose an unperfumed softener or skip it altogether.)

7) Dry each load separately (do not mix whites with colors). Again, choose the highest temperature the clothing can withstand: high for cottons, medium for permanent press, low for more delicate fabrics.

8) Remove clothes from the dryer as soon as they are finished to avoid wrinkling. Clothes that will be ironed should be hung on hangers. All other items should be folded and put away immediately. Some people are very particular about how their clothes are folded. If you are in doubt, ask, or check their drawers for examples of properly folded garments.

9) If you are drying clothes on a line outdoors, they may become stiff. A quick once-over with a warm iron will soften the fabric again.

10) Before ironing, check the garment label for specific instructions. Also check the iron before you turn it on to make sure it is clean. Cotton and linen clothes require a very hot iron, and you may need to spritz the clothes with plain water, too. (If your water contains a lot of minerals – "hard water" – use distilled or filtered water to avoid mineral stains on clothes.)

11) Ironing is not difficult, but it does require some patience and practice. Consult any of the suggested reading books for hints on ironing.

12) Finally, do not attempt to deal with clothing marked "dry clean only" by yourself. Turn them over to a professional dry cleaner. (For more information on caring for fine dress clothes, see the lesson on Ladies' Maids and Valets.)

Some fabrics (most silks and fine wools) and certain garments (stockings and other lingerie) must be washed by hand. Fill a clean sink with cool water. While the water is running, add a small amount of mild washing soap. Immerse the garments in the soapy water one at a time and squeeze the suds through the garments. Do not scrub or wring the garments. Rinse with fresh water and hang to dry. Sweaters and other items that might become misshapen if hung should be "blocked" on a drying rack. (Avoid wooden racks, as they may splinter and often decay with prolonged exposure to dampness.)

Activity: Organize your sock drawer so that you can locate any individual pair of socks by touch only. Hint: separate socks by color and weight. Use old shoe boxes or tissue boxes to separate the categories.

A short exercise: Right now, how many pairs of clean underwear do you have on hand? When you are caring for a dominant's clothing, it is important to make sure that several days' worth of outfits are in the wings at all times. Don't procrastinate with the washing. If you include laundry in your regular cleaning schedule, it will not build up and become burdensome.

Dishes

Finally, even if they are not cooking or eating in the house, slaves are frequently called upon to wash dishes. If you have the use of an electric dishwasher, you will find this a simple task. Rinse the dishes to remove any large pieces of food, then load glassware and anything marked "upper rack dishwasher safe" (some plastics) in the upper rack, and plates, pots, and pans in the lower rack. Add the dishwashing detergent (powder or liquid), close the machine, and turn it on. What could be simpler?

If you are washing dishes by hand, however, the task involves a bit more planning. Be sure to wear lined rubber gloves to spare your hands. Using hot water and dishwashing liquid, wash glassware first, then cutlery, then plates, then any pots and pans or greasy utensils. Be sure to rinse the soap off carefully, as soap that has dried on dishes can cause gastro-intestinal disturbances if ingested. Pots and pans with baked-on food or burned bottoms should be soaked in hot water with a little soap for 15-20 minutes, then washed thoroughly. You may need to use an abrasive sponge or steel wool to remove the burned food, but be sure that the pan will not be damaged by abrasion. (Heatproof glass pans and pans with non-stick coatings are delicate and should be handled with care.)

Crystal and silver should never be washed in a dishwasher. When washing crystal, put a terry cloth towel in the bottom of the sink to avoid chipping the crystal, and only use warm water. Silver should be dried immediately and stored in felt bags to minimize tarnishing.

Some fine china must also be washed by hand. Use the same technique as with crystal.

Activity: If you are accustomed to washing your dishes in a machine, try washing them by hand for a few days. Some people find the repetitive nature of the task and the sound and feel of the warm water quite soothing.

Lesson 19. Housework II: Grocery and Household Shopping

Grocery shopping is another task that many dominants are happy to turn over to a slave. Like cleaning, it is not inherently difficult, but does require some planning.

Shopping Lists

Are you the sort of person who shops by wandering down the aisles and picking up whatever looks appetizing at the moment? Do you ever shop when you're hungry? Have you ever arrived home after a trip to the supermarket only to discover that you still don't have anything to eat for dinner? If you're nodding vigorously (or blushing), please read this section carefully.

Exercise: Ideally, you'll need the help of a friend for this activity. Make up a short shopping list (5-10 items), and send your friend to the store. What does s/he return with?

You may find that while you wrote "canned corn," you really meant a 12-ounce can of Del Monte canned corn...but you got a 6-ounce can of generic creamed corn. If you don't have the aid of a friend, list a few items you regularly buy (bread, milk, cereal...) and spend some time looking at the staggering variety of items available at your local supermarket. If you wrote "milk," for example, you'll find half-and-half, whole milk, reduced fat milk (1% and 2%), skim or non-fat milk, acidophilus milk, lactose-free milk, and goat's milk, not to mention powdered (instant) milk in both whole and non-fat varieties, evaporated milk and sweetened condensed milk. Obviously, the lesson here is: Be specific.

Activity: Go through the cupboards of the kitchen you'll be shopping for (perhaps your own) and make a list of each and every item you find, including the size and brand names. Add to this list anything that you normally keep on hand but might be out of at the moment. Include spices, baking supplies, and other items that you may use infrequently. Then do the same for the refrigerator. (While you're at it, throw away any perishables that are making your kitchen look like a science lab.) Now check your cleaning and paper supplies and any toiletries and add any appropriate items to your list. You have just created a Master Shopping List.

Suggested Reading: If you are just beginning to stock a kitchen, refer to Bride's Lifetime Guide to Good Food and Entertaining, p. 6, or Dad's Own Cookbook by Bob Sloan, pp. 21-22, for lists of staples.

Activity: Go to your usual supermarket with a pad of paper and a pencil. Draw a box to represent the store and divide the box into columns to represent the aisles. In each column, write the items displayed in each aisle: produce, dairy, frozen foods, baking products, cereal.... General headings are all you need; use the overhead signs in the aisles if you need help.

Now, match up the specific items on your Master Shopping List with the schematic drawing of the supermarket. The result will look something like this:

Produce	Paper Products	Frozen Foods
bananas	Brand X toilet paper	store brand
apples	Brand Q paper towels	frozen peas
salad greens	Brand Z tissues (white)...	Len & Larry's Quadruple
fresh basil...		Chocolate ice cream...

Leave some blank spaces at the end for items you may have forgotten.

Photocopy your store-diagram-cum-shopping-list and hang one copy on the refrigerator or on inside of a cupboard door, along with a small pencil. When you run out of an item, circle it on the list. When you're ready to shop, take the list with you. It will help you speed through the store. (For information on using menus to plan your grocery shopping trips and tips on household budgeting and shopping, see "The House-keeper" in the Area Studies section.)

This system can be adapted for most stores, including drugstores, office supply stores, and large chain variety stores. The initial time investment will prove minimal compared to the savings of time and money you'll enjoy using this shopping method.

Resources: Some supermarkets are now offering computer-assisted grocery shopping. They provide software – a database of their stock – that allows you to select the items you want (and alternatives). You submit your list by e-mail and specify a delivery time. While this service can be costly, it does allow you to look at a store's offerings systematically and can be invaluable for those for whom shopping or transporting groceries is difficult.

Lesson 20. Housework III: Basic Cooking

Remember the old saying that the way to a man's heart is through his stomach? Male or female, most dominants appreciate a well-prepared meal. In addition to providing energy and nutrients for our bodies, food nourishes the soul. It can be a source of comfort as well as pleasure. What better way to care for someone than to prepare a feast for their senses?

Basic Skills

Virtually anyone can learn the basics of cooking. If you can read and follow directions, you can cook. If you're not yet comfortable in the kitchen, take some time to read about food.

Activity: Purchase or borrow a copy of one of the basic cookbooks on the suggested reading list. Don't worry about making any of the recipes yet: Just read the cookbook as a book. Note any terms or ingredients that are unfamiliar to you and make a point of finding more information on them. (The Joy of Cooking and Le Cordon Bleu Complete Cooking Techniques are good secondary reference books.)

Activity: Buy and read a cooking magazine or two. **Cook's Illustrated** is a fine publication for the beginner.

Activity: Inventory your cooking tools. You may own a single skillet and a tea kettle or a 25-piece set of professional grade cookware. List everything you have on hand. (If you will be cooking elsewhere, inventory that kitchen instead.)

Activity: Public television stations often run high-quality cooking shows by well-known chefs. Check your local programming, and watch a few. You can also record them for later viewing. Current popular shows suitable for beginners and old hands alike include "Jacques Pépin's Kitchen: Cooking with Claudine" and "Cucina Amore" (with Nick Stellino). Both feature simple, healthful recipes and focus on basic techniques. Julia Child is a perennial favorite.

Simple Classic Meals

At minimum, a slave should know how to make a few classic dishes. None of these meals takes more than an hour, including cooking time. The ingredients are all readily available at your supermarket, and the recipes – which serve at least two – can be doubled if needed. Be sure to check beforehand to see if anyone you'll be cooking for has food allergies, a dislike for any of the main flavors, or other special dietary needs.

Breakfast Muffins

1 c. flour (white or wheat)
1 c. instant oatmeal
1/4 c. sugar
2 t. baking powder
1/2 t. salt (optional)
1 c. milk
1/4 c. vegetable oil
1 egg
1 c. raisins, shredded coconut, nuts, berries, or chopped apple (optional)

Preheat the oven to 400°F. Combine dry ingredients in a bowl, then mix in wet ingredients, stirring until just combined (batter will be lumpy). Fill greased muffin tins 2/3 full. Bake approximately 20 minutes or until golden brown. Makes 1 dozen.

Variations: Substitute 3/4 c. cornmeal or crushed flake cereal for the oatmeal and increase the flour to 1 1/2 c.

Onion Soup

2 T. butter or margarine
4 c. thinly sliced onions
6 c. broth (vegetable or beef)

1/4 c. dry red wine

1/2 t. dried thyme

1/4 t. dried savory

1 bay leaf

salt and pepper to taste

Melt the butter in a large saucepan and sauté onions at medium heat until soft. Add remaining ingredients and bring to a boil. Simmer uncovered for 1 hour. Remove and discard bay leaf before serving. Serves 6 as a first course.

Variations: While the alcohol in the red wine will cook out of the soup, if you are cooking for someone who does not tolerate alcohol well, substitute 2 T. soy sauce and omit the salt.

For a simple, hearty lunch, spoon soup into an oven-safe bowl over a slice of day-old French bread. Top with grated parmesan or romano cheese and a slice of Swiss or fontina cheese. Place bowl under a broiler until the cheese is melted.

Angel Hair Pasta with Tomato Sauce

1 large (28-oz.) can diced tomatoes

4 medium peeled, chopped garlic cloves

3 T. olive oil (extra virgin is best)

2 T. coarsely chopped fresh basil leaves

1/4 t. sugar

1 1/2 t. salt

3/4 lb. capellini (angel hair)

Sauté the garlic in the olive oil until fragrant. Before the garlic turns brown, add the tomatoes and cook until thickened a bit (approx. 10 minutes). Add the basil, sugar, and salt. Cook for an additional 10 minutes.

While sauce is cooking, cook the pasta in a large pot of boiling, salted water. Capellini cooks very quickly (2 minutes); other noodles take longer. Check the package. Do not overcook the pasta; it should be *al dente* – firm to the bite.

Drain the pasta in a colander and add it to the sauce. Cook for 1 minute, then serve immediately with freshly grated parmesan or romano cheese. Serves 3, or 2 very hearty eaters.

Variations: This basic dish can be varied by including ground beef and/or veal in the sauce (brown the meat in a skillet and drain away the fat before adding to the sauce), or lightly sautéed zucchini and onions.

Roast Chicken with Vegetables

1 large roasting chicken with innards removed
8 cloves peeled garlic
1/2 t. dried thyme
8 new red potatoes, washed
2 carrots, washed, peeled, and cut into 2-inch long hunks
1 large onion
olive oil

Preheat oven to 350°F. Wash the chicken carefully and place it breast up in a baking dish. Chop the onion and combine it with the thyme, and a little olive oil. Stuff the chicken with the mixture. Cut small slits in the skin of the breast and put one garlic clove in each. Brush olive oil over the surface of the bird. Arrange potatoes and carrots around the chicken. Place pan in oven and bake until done (approximately 1 hour). To check doneness, cut into the breast with a knife down to the bone. If the chicken is white all the way through (no pink showing), it is done.

Variations: Substitute dill for the thyme. Try other root vegetables like turnips or sweet potatoes instead of or in addition to the potatoes and carrots.

Safety Warning: Always wash your hands and all utensils including the cutting board with soap immediately after handling raw chicken or other meats.

Garlic Lover's Bread

1 loaf fresh Italian bread
8-10 cloves garlic, peeled and finely diced
1/8 lb. butter

1/8 c. extra virgin olive oil

dried parsley

Melt the butter and olive oil together and mix with the garlic. Slice the bread lengthwise and spread with butter-oil-garlic mixture. Sprinkle lightly with parsley. Put the two halves of the loaf back together and wrap in foil. Heat in a 400° F. oven for 15 minutes. Unwrap and cut into 2-inch slices before serving. Serves 4-6.

Warning: This bread is a garlic lover's dream... but may be a nightmare for friends the next day. To cut the smell of garlic on the breath, drink a full glass of milk.

For a simple dessert, serve a scoop of vanilla ice cream in a dessert bowl topped with Grand Marnier, Bailey's Irish Cream, or raspberry jam that has been heated slightly.

Activity: Cook one or more of these dishes for yourself. If you enjoy them, begin a recipe file. Note any variations you try.

Suggested Reading: With literally thousands of cookbooks on the market, you could cook a different dish every night for the rest of your life and never get through them all. If you are a beginner, though, it is best to obtain one or two of the classic introductions to the art of cooking. Miss Abernathy favors The Way to Cook by the inimitable Julia Child, but the following titles will also stand you in good stead: The New Making of a Cook by Madeleine Kamman, The Joy of Cooking by Irma S. Rombauer, Marion Rombauer Becker and Ethan Becker (older editions may be preferable if you favor a classic approach), and Le Cordon Bleu Complete Cooking Techniques by Jeni Wright and Eric Treuillé. If you prefer American-style home cooking, you might try one of the Fanny Farmer, Better Homes & Gardens, or Betty Crocker cookbooks. Absolute beginners who only need to be able to make a few simple dishes might also enjoy Dad's Own Cookbook by Bob Sloan. For a list of books on wine, please see the reference book list in the chapter on Advanced Butlering.

Drinks: Coffee and Tea

A slave's ability to make a decent cup of coffee or tea is priceless. Tastes in these drinks vary greatly from person to person, and indeed from region to region, so a slave does well to inquire about a dominant's preferences.

To make coffee, start with the correct grind for the brewing method you'll be using. In general, the finer the grind, the more flavorful the coffee. A standard proportion is one tablespoon of ground coffee to six ounces of cold water for coffee machines and filter or drip methods. Avoid percolators, as they often give a metallic or burned taste to the brew. Heat the water to boiling and then pour over the coffee, making sure to soak all the grounds. Coffee can be kept hot in a thermal carafe, but should not be left on the heating unit of a coffee machine, as it will scorch and taste foul.

Coffee is usually served with cream (half-and-half in the United States) or sometimes milk, and sugar and/or artificial sweetener. A tablespoon of liqueur can be added after dinner for a sweet dessert coffee. (Flavored coffees, although they smell lovely in the shop, are often weak and tasteless once brewed.)

Tea drinkers are perhaps even more particular about their brew than coffee aficionados. Whenever possible, use loose tea rather than tea bags for the best flavor. (Metal or mesh tea balls allow the tea to expand more and so yield a fuller flavor. They also have distinct environmental advantages.) The usual proportion for a pot of tea is "one teaspoon per cup and one for the pot." Again, start with cold water. For black tea, heat the water until it just boils: Look for small bubbles. (Despite the ubiquity of the teakettle, using a saucepan makes it easier to gauge the water temperature.) Pour the water over the tea to cover and allow to steep for 3-5 minutes. Green teas require slightly cooler water and a shorter steeping time. (If you're using loose tea placed directly into the pot, remember to strain the tea as you serve it.)

Pouring the tea is a distinction usually given to the (female) guest of honor. If you are asked to pour, remember that it is traditional to put the sugar and milk into the cup first and then pour the tea in. This is because many fine teacups are very thin and the hot tea might crack them. The cool milk absorbs the heat and saves the cup. (If you are serving tea in glasses or without milk, place a metal spoon in the glass to absorb the heat.)

Black tea may be served with milk (not cream, which is too heavy and obscures the subtle flavors of the tea), sugar, honey, or lemon. Never mix lemon and milk, as the milk will curdle. Green teas are served without any additions, often in small cups.

Never re-use tea by pouring more hot water over it. This is the equivalent of adding more hot water to a pot of brewed coffee. Cold, used tea bags make wonderful eye compresses and will also absorb strong odors in the refrigerator.

Suggested Reading: The traditions surrounding afternoon tea are so rich and varied that they form the subject matter of numerous books. Among the best are The Afternoon Tea Book by Michael Smith, The London Ritz Book of Afternoon Tea by Helen Simpson, and The Pleasures of Afternoon Tea by Angela Hynes. All contain some background on the history of British teas as well as recipes and menu suggestions.

IV. AREA STUDIES

Congratulations! You have completed the basic skills training and household management sections of the course and are moving into more specialized work. If you've taken care to complete the exercises up to this point, you are prepared to make some more informed decisions about the direction your training as a slave will take.

Early on in lesson 2, you were asked to take a brief diagnostic test to help you get some ideas about the different kinds of slaves and your own interests and natural abilities. Please review that lesson now, and re-take the test. You may find that after several months of training, you know yourself better and your ideas have changed. Note which type(s) of slavehood most appeal to you, and proceed to those areas below.

Even if you know beyond the shadow of a doubt that you want to be a sex slave or a lady's maid, please at least read through the information and exercises in the other sections. As I indicated in the introduction to the Household Management section, most slaves are expected to perform some type of domestic service, and it is to your benefit to have at least a working knowledge of what is required to run a house. Likewise, even if you already have a clear arrangement with a dominant that genital sex will never be a part of your relationship, you would do well to review the information in the lessons for sex slaves, as it contains ideas that may help you develop a more holistic view of sexuality.

Again, congratulations on your work thus far.

SEX SLAVES

Sex is a natural part of being human. It exists both for reproductive purposes and for the joy it brings us. Many slaves-in-training first became aware of their submissive natures in a sexual context and for most, sex remains an important part of their experience of slavehood.

Sex Workers as Role Models

If you have chosen to focus your training on the sexual arena, you have much work ahead of you. Many beginners think being a sex slave is a life of leisure: after all, you have sex all the time, right? What could be better? Unfortunately, no one can have sex for hours and hours every day without it becoming tiresome, even boring. Ask any sex worker: sex is hard work.

In fact, sex workers are your role models now. Just as accountants deal with numbers and finances, and builders deal with materials, plans, and tools, sex workers deal – professionally, day in and day out – with sexuality, both their own and other people's. If they take their job seriously, and many do, they spend time and energy learning how to do that job better. They read and take classes, they talk shop with their peers, they form alliances and professional organizations.

At its best, sex work can become a spiritual calling, a vocation in the highest sense. Sex workers are healers and priest/esses. They take a powerful experience – sex – and use it to move themselves and others into ecstasy and communion with the divine. As a sex slave, you too can become a healer, a mediator of spiritual energy.

Sex Slave Psychology

If you've lead an active sex life thus far, you may be wondering what makes a sex slave different from any other healthy man or woman with a reasonably high sex drive. Is it just a matter of some play-acting?

What distinguishes a sex slave from any other lover is part of what distinguishes a houseboy from a professional domestic: attitude. While lovers may certainly derive satisfaction from pleasing their partners, they generally want to experience some pleasure for themselves. If that pleasure is denied, they will feel slighted, at very least, and may simply write off their partner as "selfish" or "not a very talented lover." A sex slave, on the other hand, makes him- or herself available for the dominant's pleasure with no expectation of physical gratification for themselves. Their satisfaction lies in serving, not in orgasm.

For a slave, sex is a service on par with cooking, cleaning, and personal attendance. It does not carry with it any greater respect than polishing boots, cooking a soufflé, or scrubbing the floor. It is service, period. It is important to recognize that all of these activities have equal value and require dedication, intelligence, and skill.

You should bear in mind, however, that to allow themselves to be served, dominants enter into a pact of trust with their slaves and must rely on their discretion and integrity. This is especially true of sex slaves, since physical intimacy is often equated with vulnerability in our sexual economy. Likewise, the slave must trust that the dominant has the slave's best interests and well-being in mind. In addition to the satisfaction of serving, you may eventually earn the honor of more complete trust from the dominant. For this you should strive.

Self-Care for Sex Slaves

Sex slaves need to attend to self-care, perhaps more than any other kind of slave. If you've been running around all day polishing silver, it's assumed you'll want to rest. It's easy to think that sex slaves live a life of leisure and pleasure and don't need any time to relax. Nothing could be further from the truth. Sexual energy is perhaps the most powerful we humans know and working with it can cause "burnout." Again, ask any sex worker.

As you work through this material, be sure to take plenty of time for yourself. Take frequent walks and long, soaking baths. Attend carefully to your meditation and consider yoga or tai chi to help balance your body and psyche. Because you may spend more time naked, you will want to pay special attention to your personal hygiene; some of the lessons below will cover personal care issues of special interest to sex slaves. Most of all, be sure to communicate with your trainer (as well as in your slave journal) about any emotional or physical changes that you experience.

A Note on Safer Sex

As part of your training contract, you may have negotiated an agreement about safer sex. As a sex slave, the practical aspects of safer sex may often be left to you. It behooves you to understand what types of sexual behaviors leave you and your partner(s) at risk for disease transmission and to take appropriate precautions. All of the general sex manuals and beginning SM books listed below will give you the basics of safer sex. Use them wisely. See also The New Our Bodies, Ourselves by the Boston Women's Health Book Collective and Total Health for Men ed. Neil Wertheimer. The Complete Guide to Safe Sex video is another good resource and covers all orientations as well as BDSM.

Resources: San Francisco Sex Information provides referrals and information on sex-related topics by phone (not phone sex!). They can be reached at (415) 929-7374.

Suggested Reading: Begin with one or two general sex manuals. The Good Vibrations Guide to Sex by Cathy Winks and Anne Semans is down-to-earth, pansexual, and more woman-focused than some other books. The Joy of...Sex series (ed. Alex Comfort), available for gay men and lesbians as well as heterosexuals, are classic guides, illustrated with realistic drawings. The Ultimate Sex Book by therapist Anne Hooper is also copiously illustrated and relatively well-disposed toward erotic role-play. Although many of the techniques are not gender specific, the book maintains a definite heterosexual focus. Further, the photographs (all of young, thin, white models) are rather sanitized, with no full frontal nudity. Pat Califia's classic Sapphistry is an excellent basic sex guide for lesbians and is filled with the no-nonsense, sex-positive attitude and crisp writing that have made the author famous.

Many collections of sex tips are available. Among the best are Jay Wiseman's lighthearted Tricks, Tricks 2, Sex Toy Tricks, and Supermarket Tricks, and Sex Tips for Straight Women from a Gay Man by Dan Anderson and Maggie Berman. The New Male Sexuality by Bernie Zilbergeld is also helpful.

Some basic books on BDSM should also be part of any sex slave's library. SM 101 by Jay Wiseman, Sensuous Magic by Pat Califia, Learning the Ropes by Race Bannon, and The Lesbian SM Safety Manual, ed. Califia, are all noteworthy for their sanity, readability, and emphasis on physical and emotional safety, not to mention the sheer volume of information between their covers.

Sex slaves should read all the erotica they can get their hands on, including "real life fantasy" collections like His Secret Life *by Bob Berkowitz and* My Secret Garden *and* Women on Top *by Nancy Friday. See Manual, pp. 71-75 for an annotated guide to BDSM classics. While erotica is not always the best source for sex tips — some of what excites in print may be dangerous, illegal, or simply impossible in real life — it is an excellent resource for fantasy and gives the reader insight into the workings of the erotic imagination.*

Finally, take the time to read some of the ground-breaking writing by and about sex workers that has appeared in the last few years. Self-aware and -empowered sex workers can be role models for sex slaves. Whores and Other Feminists, *ed. Jill Nagle, is a snappy and hard-hitting anthology of essays and personal narratives by self-identified feminist sex workers and their allies. Also recommended is* Sex Work: Writings by Women in the Sex Industry *by Frédérique Delacoste and Priscilla Alexander.*

Suggested Viewing: There are many high quality sex education videos available; these aren't the mortifying "where babies come from" films you saw in health class. If you have difficulty finding any of these videos in your area, contact the Good Vibrations Video Library Mail Order Department for a catalogue or to place an order: (415) 974-8990, 7 a.m.-7 p.m., every day except Sunday.

Lesson 21. Personal Care I: Shaving

For many people, shaving their pubic hair is highly erotic. Hairiness is sometimes considered "animal" or "virile" and equated with strong sex drive or an "active" role; hairlessness suggests vulnerability, a winning quality in a slave. A hairless pubis may also suggest youth and innocence. Shaving also makes visible that which is usually hidden and private, and some submissives enjoy the feeling of "complete nakedness" that shaving brings.

Exercise: Complete the following sentences.

When I imagine myself without pubic hair, I feel...

My hair is...

If I were shaved, I'd be embarrassed to...

Women with no pubic hair look...

Men with no pubic hair look...

As a slave, my pubic hair...

I'd shave, except...

If I were ordered to shave, I'd...

Activity: Remove your pubic hair by shaving or wax treatment. If you hair is very long or thick, trim it first with blunt-tipped scissors or electric clippers. Go slowly. Then soak in a warm tub for about 15 minutes. This will open your pores and make shaving easier. Start with a new disposable safety razor. Apply a mild soap lather or shaving cream to the area and shave using short strokes in the same direction as the hair grows. (For the closest possible shave, you will need to shave against the direction of growth; save this for last.) You may need to pull looser skin taut and use a good magnifying mirror for areas you can't easily see. If you nick yourself, be sure to wash the area carefully and apply a dab of anti-bacterial ointment.

If you find you have strong negative feelings about being completely shaven, try just trimming your pubic hair. This will give you a neat appearance and is a good aid to hygiene. Women may want to experiment with the "ice cream cone cut," where the hair on the mons is trimmed short (often in a neat triangle or strip) and the hair on the outer labia is shaved.

You may experience some itching as the hair begins to grow back; apply talcum powder to the area to reduce the itch. Particularly if your hair is very curly, you'll want to wash the area daily with warm water, mild soap, and a terry washcloth to prevent ingrown hairs. (Some people prefer a loofah sponge; use it gently to avoid irritation.) People who shave regularly report that the itching becomes less bothersome as your skin adjusts to being shaved. If you find that shaving irritates your skin, you may want to try other depilation methods like waxing or hair removal creams. Visit a salon for help, or read the package instructions carefully if you're removing hair at home.

Activity: Experiment with shaving other parts of your body. Always begin with a fresh razor and lots of warm water.

Lesson 22. Personal Care II: Cleansing Enemas and Douches

Enemas play a role in many people's sexual fantasies: the Naughty Nurse with her rolling enema cart is a popular dominant persona. But aside from fantasy fulfillment, what practical reasons are there for using enemas? I see two functions that relate to slaves.

The primary reason is to make anal sex (including the use of anal plugs) more comfortable and aesthetically pleasing. Fecal matter contains bacteria and can be gritty, making anal sex both irritating to the rectum and potentially dangerous. Many people find the smell and sight of feces unpleasant, too. The solution: cleansing enemas.

The second reason enemas find their way into slave training is that many slaves find that receiving an enema, particularly when administered by a dominant, enhances their submission. Our culture attaches a great deal of shame to the anus, and allowing another person to control this part of the body can induce deeply submissive feelings.

It is important to remember that the bowel is quite delicate and must be treated with care. Cleansing enemas should be gently administered using warm water and low pressure. It usually takes no more than one quart of water to clean out the lower bowel for anal play. Introduce the water slowly and pause if you feel any cramping. Give yourself plenty of time to release the water and waste, too.

Safety Warnings: It isn't necessary to add anything to the water, and indeed, some additives are very dangerous. Alcohol in enemas can be fatal! The only exception to this rule is salt. Some people suggest dissolving one-half teaspoon or so of table salt in each quart of water to help replace the salts depleted by the enema process; several glasses of water or electrolyte-fortified "sports beverages" drunk after the process will also help balance fluids in the system.)

While the occasional use of enemas isn't thought to be harmful, over-use can lead to weakened bowel function and dependence on enemas for elimination. High colonics also deplete important digestive flora; eat a cup of live-culture yogurt to replace them.

Activity: Purchase an enema bag – many are marketed as "hot water bottles with attachments." Assemble the bag and clean it before use by filling with warm water and one tablespoon of white vinegar (acetic acid solution). Let this solution run through the bag; repeat two more times with clean water.

Now you are ready to administer a cleansing enema. (Some people find it helpful to drink a cup of coffee first, as it stimulates the bowel, but this is not necessary.) Fill the bag with warm water (test it on the inside of your elbow) and hang no more than 6-8 inches above the anus. Most people find it easiest to do this in the bathtub. Put a towel in the bottom of the tub for cushioning and lie on your left side. Lubricate the nozzle before insertion. Once the nozzle is inserted, release the water using the clamp on the hose. Go as slowly as you want and stop the flow if you feel a cramp. It will pass. When you feel full – which might be after a few ounces or a whole quart – remove the nozzle. Carefully get out of the tub and sit on the toilet until you've released all the waste water. For anal sex, you will want to repeat this process until the water comes out clear. Be sure to drink some fluids afterwards.

Like enemas, douches are sometimes used before sex for hygiene. The vagina is a self-cleaning organ, producing a small amount of normal fluid daily. (This is the regular clear discharge you find on your panties.) In general, douches do more harm than good, as they change the natural pH of the vagina and can make some women more susceptible to yeast infections. They also flush out vaginal lubrication which is vital for comfortable intercourse. However, some women use a cleansing douche toward the end of their periods to flush away any remaining menstrual blood. If you do douche, be sure to use the appropriate nozzle (it has a series of small holes on the sides and is flared), warm water, a very small amount of white vinegar if desired, and gentle pressure. You can squat in the tub or shower or hang the bag near the toilet. Insert the nozzle a few inches into your vagina and release the water flow.

Safety Warnings: Avoid commercial solutions with added fragrances, as many women are violently allergic to them. If you notice any unusual discharge, see your doctor, as this may be a sign of infection.

Lesson 23. Sexual Stamina: Controlling Orgasm

As a slave, you have given control of yourself to another person. This includes the use of your sexual drives. Many dominants enjoy dictating when and how a slave may orgasm, so it is to your benefit to become aware of your own patterns of sexual response and to learn to direct them.

To this end, Miss Abernathy suggests several exercises to strengthen your pelvic muscles and to control the flow of sexual energy during arousal. You will obtain the best results if you undertake these exercises as regular, daily practices. Neither is complex, but both – particularly together – can have an enormous impact on your sexual self-control.

The first exercise is designed to strengthen the pubococcygeus or PC muscle. The PC muscle is located in the pelvis and supports the genitals, urethra, and anus. The PC muscle controls the flow of urine, so when you are next urinating, try to stop the flow. By doing so, you're contracting your PC muscle. This is also the muscle that contracts rhythmically during orgasm. Like any other muscle, the PC muscle needs regular exercise to function well.

Activity: Squeeze your PC muscle tight and then release. Try ten quick contractions (count one *one thousand* and release) followed by ten longer contractions (three to ten seconds). These contractions – often called "Kegels" after the doctor who discovered the importance of the PC muscle for sexual health – should be done several times a day. Kegels are unnoticeable to others, so you can practice them at any time and in any place.

In addition to physically strengthening your sexual organs, to control orgasm you need to control your sexual response. The following exercise is derived from Tantra, a spiritual path that incorporates meditation and ritualized sex to help the practitioners achieve a blissful state.

Tantra teaches that what we normally identify as orgasm – the explosive pleasure of genital contractions and, in men, ejaculation – is only one step on the ladder of sexual pleasure, and a relatively low step at that. By using our breath, we can move sexual energy from its usual seat in the pelvic region up along energy channels in the body until it floods our heart and brain centers. Tantra practitioners claim that this flow of energy to the brain causes a change in brain function that leads to ecstatic states. This energy can also be directed to various organs in the body for healing and pleasure. The practice introduced here will help you transform "explosive" orgasms to "implosive" ones (as Tantrika Margo Anand calls them) which, with practice, will help you prolong the sex act as long as you like.

Activity: Find a time when you can be alone and undisturbed for at least an hour. Recline on a bed or some other comfortable place; you may want a pillow under your head or hips. Begin by taking ten long, deep breaths. As you do so, become aware of how your breath moves from your nose down into your lungs. Feel the way your belly rises with the incoming breath and falls again as you exhale. Continue to breathe deeply from your diaphragm.

Using warm massage oil or your favorite lubricant, begin to massage your genitals until you feel aroused. Continue to stimulate yourself as you become aware of the sexual energy building in your pelvic region. You may sense a tightness or fullness. Now, gently massage your perineum, the area just in front of the anus. Take a deep breath and draw the sexual energy from your pelvis into the perineum. (You might imagine the energy as a pool of light or sense it as warmth – whatever image works best for you is the right one.) As you continue to masturbate, take another deep breath and imagine the energy traveling up your spine and pooling at a spot on the spine behind your navel. With the next breath, the energy will move up to the base of your neck. Another breath with take the energy to the crown of your head. Now breathe again as the energy spills over your forehead, pooling between your eyes. The next breath brings the energy down into your chest and the heart region. Pause here and let the energy collect, then release it back into your lower belly.

As you continue to stimulate yourself, follow the energy path through your body: from the perineum, up the spine to the head, down the front of your body to the heart and the belly and over your genitals back down to the perineum.

Now, when you find yourself approaching orgasm, stop the stimulation, but breathe even more deeply and slowly and allow the energy to keep flowing. Relax your muscles and release any tension. Then begin to stimulate yourself again. Finally, you may approach orgasm and feel that you are being pushed "over the top": as best you can, stop the stimulation and breathe deeply, consciously moving the orgasmic energy along the pathway to your head. You will experience a very different type of orgasm. Instead of a deep throbbing or contractions focused in your genital area, you'll feel a rush of energy in your head and chest. Best of all, this rush will not subside after fifteen or even thirty seconds, but with practice can be sustained for minutes at a time. (Adepts talk of four-hour orgasms.)

Men may notice that they do not ejaculate when they have this type of orgasm, and so they can maintain their erections for much longer. Both men and women will find that instead of feeling exhausted and sleepy after orgasm, they feel energized yet relaxed.

If while practicing this exercise you have a "normal" orgasm, enjoy it and don't indulge in self-criticism. Tantric practitioners spend years learning these techniques. Take up the exercise again another day.

The benefit of this exercise for slaves is the ability, over time, to delay "explosive" orgasms indefinitely, while still enjoying pleasurable (and healthful) feelings. You will ultimately find that you can access sexual energy without direct genital stimulation and can experience some of the same sensations even when you have been forbidden to touch yourself.

Suggested Reading: The Art of Sexual Ecstasy by Margo Anand introduces Tantric techniques in accessible language and with great sensitivity.

Suggested Viewing: Ancient Secrets of Sexual Ecstasy for Modern Lovers (heterosexual focus) and The Art of Extending Orgasm (heterosexual and lesbian couples) both teach Tantric exercises.

Lesson 24. Sexual Service I: Masturbation and Erotic Touch

Many dominants are unabashed voyeurs. Part of the thrill of control is watching a submissive carry out a task. And that includes sex. Slaves are often called upon to "perform" for a dominant by stripping or masturbating.

Activity: Find a time and place where you won't be disturbed. Dress up in your sexiest outfit and put on some erotic music. Lower the lights, if it makes you feel good. Allow yourself to move sensuously to the music. Run your hands over your body. Slowly remove your clothes, garment by garment. When you are naked, begin to masturbate. Stretch out on the floor or the bed and let yourself go.

Try this exercise several times or until you are comfortable with it. (Experiment with different outfits and music.) Then, try stripping in front of a full-length mirror. If you are shy at first, try positioning the mirror so you can't see your own face. Watch yourself masturbate. Notice the way your genitals look; listen to the sounds you make as you become more and more excited. Discover what positions and poses look erotic to you.

Activity: Visit a strip club (men's or women's). Enjoy the show and notice how the dancers move. Can you use of these moves in your own private "strip show"?

Suggested Reading: Sex for One by Betty Dodson is a virtual masturbation manifesto. It is an excellent introduction to the fine art of self-loving and also contains good advice for those who are pre-orgasmic. If you feel foolish or frightened of performing, try Carol Queen's Exhibitionism for the Shy, a warm and witty guide to awakening your inner exhibitionist. Men Loving Themselves by Jack Morin and I Am My Lover: Women Pleasure Themselves, ed. Joani Blank, are beautifully photographed studies of men and women masturbating.

Resources: The Learning Annex, which has branches in most major American cities, regularly offers personal enrichment courses on "How to Strip for Your Lover."

A good sex slave should know how to pleasure a dominant in as many ways as possible. Among these, erotic touch is the most important, as it plays a role in all the more obvious forms of sex play.

Exercise: List ten different items (including body parts) with which you could touch someone erotically: feather, long hair, velvet....

Activity: Collect 6-8 different items from your list above and put them in a box. When you next masturbate, close your eyes (or blindfold yourself) and choose something from the box. Touch your nipples, your belly, your face with it.

Activity: Get a professional, non-erotic massage. Notice the different types of touch the massage therapist uses. Which felt good to you? Did you find any of them erotic? You may also want to visit an erotic masseur or masseuse; some sex workers will be happy to teach you skills, particularly if you explain your circumstances. (Please be aware of any laws in your area regarding sex work before undertaking this activity and use your best judgment.)

Suggested Reading: The Complete Illustrated Guide to Massage by Stewart Mitchell is an excellent general introduction, and Anne Hooper's Massage and Loving is good for a more erotic focus.

Suggested Viewing: The Intimate Guide to Male Genital Massage. The movie 9 1/2 Weeks, although profoundly ambivalent about dominance and submission, does contain a few erotically charged scenes involving the sense of touch and food. If you are a pre-orgasmic woman, you'll find Becoming Orgasmic a reassuring and helpful video. You may also enjoy Betty Dodson's Selfloving. For information on using vibrators, watch Carol Queen's Great Vibrations.

Lesson 25. Clothing, Restraint, and Chastity Devices

As a sex slave, you must maintain a constant awareness both of your status as property and of your role as a sex toy. Much BDSM fiction would have us believe that sex slaves do nothing all day but pleasure voluptuous libertines. Even if you are a live-in slave serving more than one dominant, it is very likely you'll have other tasks as well. How can you maintain your submission when you're walking the dog or picking up the dry cleaning? This is a challenge for all slaves, but I mention it here because of all the specialized roles, sex slaves seem to have the most difficulty with it, perhaps because their role is essentially private. House servants may come and go more freely and are likely to deal with a wide variety of people in the course of their daily routines. They may get outside approval for their efficiency or skill. A sex slave's skills are not regularly displayed outside the privacy of the dominant's house.

With this challenge in mind, some dominants choose to outfit their slaves with unobtrusive items of clothing or chastity devices as ways of emphasizing their control and the slave's submission. Most often, the clothing is in the form of undergarments and may have a restraining character, like a corset. It may also have a cross-dressing element, as when a businessman is made to wear stockings and garters under his banker's grays. In this lesson, you'll experiment with such "hidden items."

Activity: Wear a tight-fitting undergarment today. It should be an item you usually do not wear, and it should not restrict your breathing. (Spandex bicycling shorts or a leotard are good choices.)

At the end of the day, answer these questions: How did wearing this garment change your day? Were you aware of the garment? Did it affect your ability to perform any tasks? Did you find the restriction in any way erotic? What if the garment were a corset, waist-training belt, or (for a man) pantyhose? Do you find that wearing any of these garments makes you feel especially submissive? Are you still able to carry on with your normal activities such as shopping or running errands?

Now, try wearing pantyhose (if you're a man) or a jockstrap (if you're a woman). Is your erotic response different?

Notes on Corsetry

Once a mainstay of a woman's wardrobe, the corset is now firmly in the domain of fetishists and body modification artists. Since it is such a popular item in the BDSM community and figures so greatly into the mythology of sex, I mention it here.

Activity: Visit a corsetier and, if possible, try on a corset. (Men may be surprised to hear that many corsetmakers also have designs specifically for them!)

Suggested Reading: Fans of corsetry will enjoy Support and Seduction: A History of Corsets and Bras by Béatrice Fontanel, a lushly illustrated coffee table book. The best source of information on waist-training and corsetry with an eye to dominance and submission is Body Play and Modern Primitives Quarterly, published by piercing instructor and body modification artist Fakir Musafar.

Suggested Viewing: The opening scenes of Gone with the Wind see Scarlett being laced into her corset.

Resources: Waist-training belts are available from Romantasy in San Francisco; they also make corsets: phone (415) 673-3137. Body Play regularly lists corset-makers as well.

Chastity Devices

Chastity devices are another way for dominants to assert their erotic control. If you've been working with the Tantric exercises suggested in one of the previous lessons, you will be developing greater control over your sexual energies. Chastity devices can be an exquisite way to increase that control.

The most common chastity device for men is a penis restraint or "cock cage." Usually made of leather or metal, this item is fastened around the penis and testicles and prevents the man from touching his penis, while allowing him to urinate. Chastity "belts" for women usually fasten around the waist or hips and block access to the clitoris and vagina; they also allow the woman to urinate.

See also the next lesson, on anal plugs.

Lesson 26. Anal Plugs

Review Lesson 22 on Enemas.

Anal or "butt" plugs are another common device used to control
sexual response and induce a submissive mindset. By increasing the size of
the plugs over a period of time, it is also possible to train the body to
more easily accommodate larger items and enjoy anal intercourse.

Anal plugs come in a delightful array of shapes and sizes. If you are
just beginning to explore anal play, choose a small plug. Silicone toys tend
to hold body heat well and are quite resilient.

**Safety Warning: Anal plugs should be smooth, with no sharp edges or seams, and
should have a flared base. They should not be made of any breakable material.
Always use a water-soluble lubricant with rubber toys. If you suffer from
hemorrhoids, be careful with any kind of anal play, as friction will exacerbate your
condition. Use plenty of lubricant and keep a good hemorrhoid medicine on hand.
Of the over-the-counter preparations, Anusol seems to work the best.**

Activity: Purchase a good quality anal plug. You may even want to buy one
small one and one somewhat larger one "to grow into." Some anal plugs
have graduated "bulbs" or "beads" for a one-size-fits-all effect.

Spend some time exploring your anus. You may want to take a warm bath
and a gentle enema. Trim your nails and file them down so there are no
sharp edges, or wear a latex glove if you have long nails. Warm some lubricant
in your hand and massage your anal area, including the perineum, the space
just in front of the anus. Circle the wrinkled outer surface of the anus with

your finger. Slowly insert your finger. You may also want to stimulate your penis or clitoris. Allow your finger to rest just inside the sphincter. Can you feel your pulse? Experiment to see if you enjoy the sensation of fullness more, or whether you crave movement. When you feel ready, apply lubricant to the plug and begin to insert it very slowly. Stop if you feel any pain. Your sphincter may try to clamp down on the plug. Breathe deeply and relax, while you stimulate your clitoris or penis. When your anus has gotten used to the fullness, continue. Some people find a twisting or screwing motion makes insertion easier.

Don't worry if it takes you several sessions before you can insert the plug all the way. Once you have it in, relax for a while. You may want to masturbate, or just observe the sensations. Try walking around; a properly shaped plug won't come out.

As you become more accustomed to anal plugs, you may want to experiment with wearing them for longer periods of time. This can be rewarding, but be sure to allow yourself to have bowel movements as necessary.

Suggested Reading: Anal Pleasure and Health by Jack Morin has become something of a classic in the field. It will provide you with basic information on anatomy and safety.

Suggested Viewing: Self Anal Massage for Men.

Lesson 27. Sexual Service II: Oral Service

Not all that long ago, oral sex was considered wild, a sexual taboo. (Frighteningly enough, it is technically illegal in some American states even today, falling under the rubric of "sodomy.") Still, the sexual revolution made oral lovemaking an acceptable and expected part of the erotic repertoire. And judging from the reports of dominatrices and phone sex workers, providing oral service to a dominant is one of the most common submissive fantasies.

Why? Because oral sex is focused on the pleasure of the receiver, not the giver. Although s/he may derive some gratification and pleasure from the act, the slave serving a dominant orally must postpone his or her own orgasm, perhaps indefinitely. The dominant remains the center of attention and pleasure.

Activity: Buy a selection of ripe fruit, including, if possible, strawberries, peaches, bananas, and mangoes, as well as some whipping cream. Wash and peel the fruits as needed and arrange them attractively in a bowl. Whip the cream with a little sugar until it peaks. Now repair to the bedroom.

Take off your clothes and have a towel handy. Begin by taking a piece of fruit and dipping it into the cream. Notice the beautiful contrast of the deep red of the berries or the vibrant yellow-orange of the mango and the pale white of the cream. Run your tongue along the fruit, licking off the cream. Note the texture of the fruit, its scent, its rich juices. Put the fruit in your mouth and feel the cream melt against your tongue. Linger over the subtle flavors.

Adorn your naked body with fruit. Use the banana to paint your nipples and belly with cream, then lick the banana clean. Decorate yourself with berries. Let your now sticky-sweet finger trail between your legs, along your thighs. Stroke your genitals. As you pleasure yourself, enjoy the taste of the fruit as it mingles with your own flavors. Focus on the softness of your mouth and the sweetness of the fruit. As you climax, pay attention to your tongue and lips: are they more sensitive? (Feel free to share this activity with a friend, too.)

Now, taste your own sexual fluids. Are they salty? Sweet? Pungent?

Activity: Along with oral sex, slaves are often called upon to perform other kinds of oral service. For this activity you will need a leather shoe or boot. Kneel down and put your hand inside the shoe with your fingers in the toe area. Now make love to the shoe with your mouth. As you do so, pay attention to the sensations your hand feels. How much pressure should you apply? How much is too much? Rub your cheek against the side of the shoe – can you feel it inside? Experiment with different kinds of footwear: thick engineer boots require a very different oral touch from fine leather pumps.

Activity: Practice flicking your tongue over and around the tip of your forefinger. Make circles as well as up-and-down and side-to-side motions.

Activity: Use a life-like dildo to practice your technique.

By building up the sensitivity of your lips and tongue, you are preparing yourself to give more subtle oral service. If you don't have someone to practice your technique on, please watch the video listed in "suggested viewing" carefully.

Suggested Viewing: Nina Hartley's Guide to Oral Sex: Porn star and registered nurse Nina Hartley gives a caring and joyful introduction to fellatio and cunnilingus in this video. Highly recommended.

Safety Warning: There is no consensus within the medical community about whether HIV, the virus believed to cause AIDS, can be transmitted during unprotected oral sex. However, we do know that other STDs, such as herpes, are transmitted by oral-genital contact. The best way to avoid all of these diseases – barring abstinence – is to use a latex barrier (condom or dental dam) during oral sex.

Lesson 28. Sexual Service III: Vaginal

In addition to serving a dominant woman with your mouth, you may be called upon to pleasure her vaginally. The important point to keep in mind here is that the dominant's sexual pleasure is always primary. Of course, this is also the case if you are a female slave who is required to make her body available for use by a dominant.

Exercise: List at least five ways that you could pleasure a woman vaginally without a penis.

Sex Toys: Dildos and Vibrators

Although dildos are depicted in ancient art and are among the oldest sexual artifacts we possess, they maintain a certain mystique. Vibrators are a much more recent invention, of course, and were first used not as "sports massagers," but to treat "hysteria" in female patients. Apparently doctors discovered that a good orgasm or twelve went a long way toward relieving the stresses of Victorian life.

If you are honored with the opportunity to pleasure a dominant woman with a dildo or vibrator, try to think of the toy as an extension of yourself. The dominant will undoubtedly direct you, but imagine the dildo as part of your sex or hand; think of the vibrator as your ideal tongue.

Activity: Visit a sex toy store and learn about the variety of products on the market. (If visiting a store is not an option in your area, please study the suggested reading volume carefully.) What are the advantages of a battery-operated vibrator? The disadvantages? What kind of lubricants are compatible with silicone dildos? Which dildos can be used with a harness?

Suggested Reading: The Good Vibrations Guide to Sex by Cathy Winks and Anne Semans gives a good overview of the different types of sex toys available.

Suggested Viewing: For information on using vibrators, watch Carol Queen's Great Vibrations.

Activity: If you don't already own one, purchase a vibrator. Use it when you masturbate to get a sense of its advantages. (Male slaves can also enjoy vibrators!)

The Penis as Sex Toy

Some male slaves report that they find it difficult to maintain a submissive attitude when asked to pleasure a dominant woman sexually. Since some people feel that sex is inherently degrading, especially for women, these men may feel that they must become "aggressive" when they have intercourse with a woman. Even when their submission is utterly sincere, it may be a challenge to overcome this false programming.

Remember that the dominant's pleasure is primary; your role is to facilitate and augment her enjoyment of the act. Your penis belongs to her just as fully as the rest of you. It is *her* toy. Practice the Tantric exercise given earlier in this section as a way of controlling your own orgasm.

Activity: Use a penis restraint (cock ring or cock cage) as a reminder to yourself that your penis is for Mistress's pleasure.

Activity: If you have difficulty controlling your orgasm, create a cassette tape to use during masturbation. Choose a phrase that expresses your submission ("Mistress's pleasure is my reward," for example) and record your voice saying it slowly and clearly. If you find that you normally orgasm after five minutes, record the phrase for six minutes, followed by the command: "Come now!" Then repeat the process, allowing an additional minute each time.

This exercise will teach you to control your sexual response by associating it with a certain phrase. Then, when you are called upon to pleasure your Mistress, repeat the phrase silently in your head.

Safety Warning: With all the (justifiable) concern these days with disease prevention, Miss Abernathy finds it important to remind you of another delicate matter: pregnancy. If you are engaging in activities that might lead to pregnancy and do not wish to parent a child, please use an appropriate contraceptive.

Vaginal Fisting

Miss Abernathy must admit that in matters of fisting, a picture really is worth a thousand words. Luckily, there exists a fine book that has both in abundance. If you are new to fisting, please read the volume listed in the suggested reading section of this lesson before proceeding.

"Fisting," a rather unfortunate term for this delicate art, is simply inserting one's whole hand into a woman's open and willing vagina. It requires sensitivity, good communication, and copious quantities of lubricant. Feeling a woman's body open to receive your hand is a quite incomparable experience, both awe-inspiring and humbling, and a slave who is offered an opportunity to experience it should feel honored.

Some people discover fisting quite by accident. A lover has inserted a finger or two, and as the woman becomes more excited, she asks for

"More, more!" After four fingers, the only option is to tuck the thumb under and push slowly until the muscles at the mouth of the vagina open sufficiently to allow your hand entry. For some women, only the slightest movement of the hand will induce orgasms by the dozen; others prefer a gentle in-and-out or twisting motion. Some enjoy a vigorous romp on your hand. In all cases, large amounts of lubricant are in order. (Avoid lubricants that contain nonoxynol-9, as it appears many women are violently allergic to it.) The use of latex (or, for the latex-sensitive, nitrile) gloves for this activity is also recommended, first for reasons of safer sex, but also because it seems to decrease the chance of urinary tract infections. Women who enjoy being fisted will benefit from drinking extra fluids and taking cranberry extract tablets (available at health food stores) if they are prone to urinary irritation.

If you are a female slave whose Owner enjoys fisting you, there are ways you can train your body to be more receptive.

Activity: Obtain a number of dildos of varying sizes. You may also want to include some larger anal plugs. Using lubricant, insert a dildo that is a comfortable fit and masturbate for a while. If you feel your vaginal muscles clenching the dildo, consciously relax them. As you become more excited, your vagina will open and become more elastic. Try inserting progressively larger dildos over a period of time. Please note that your menstrual cycle may well affect your comfort level with this exercise. Be aware of changes in your body and do not force anything.

Suggested Reading: A Hand in the Bush: The Fine Art of Vaginal Fisting by Deborah Addington is the only book-length introduction to this delightful practice.

G-Spot Stimulation

One of the many advantages of fisting and other manual play is that it allows for easy stimulation of the G-spot, the spongy area on the front wall of the vagina that responds, in some women, very positively to massage. (The G-spot has been compared to the male prostate gland in terms of erotic sensation.) Stimulating the G-spot seems in turn to stimulate the portion of the clitoris that is internal, and for some women, induces a very deep, intense orgasm. Orgasm may be accompanied by "female ejaculation," a spray of clear liquid from within the vagina. (In the past, some people have taken this liquid to be urine, although recent studies indicate that it is akin to seminal fluid.)

Women with active G-spots may enjoy massage with fingers, vibrators, or dildos. Sexual positions that allow a penis or dildo to ride "high", rubbing against the front wall of the vagina, can also stimulate the area. (These positions may also irritate the urethra, so women who are troubled with urinary tract infections may want to try other methods of G-spot stimulation.)

Suggested Viewing: The Complete Guide to Sexual Positions demonstrates one hundred different positions for heterosexual couples, many of which can be adapted for female partners who enjoy dildo play. How to Female Ejaculate (various orientations) and Incredible G-Spot (heterosexual focus) include techniques for G-spot stimulation. Private Pleasures and Shadows, a lesbian-made video, contains a beautiful vaginal fisting scene.

Lesson 29. Sexual Service IV: Anal

If you've tried the exercises suggested in the lessons on enemas and anal plugs, you will already have learned quite a bit about your body and its responses to anal stimulation. If you are called upon to be the receptive partner in anal sex, you will need to do two things: relax and communicate. Working with anal plugs will have taught you how to relax the sphincter; breathe deeply and push out. (Pushing out may seem counterintuitive, but it opens the sphincter.)

Communication is a more subtle issue. If you experience any pain, you must immediately tell the dominant, but you should do so in a way that is both respectful and direct: Mistress! The dildo is at a painful angle, Mistress! or Master! May I have more lube, please, Master? Anal tissue is very delicate, and it is sometimes hard for the active partner to gauge your needs from body cues alone.

Likewise, if after being used anally you notice any bleeding or other problems, inform the dominant immediately! It isn't unusual for small tears to cause slight bleeding – this can also occur after a hard, dry bowel movement, you'll notice – but it is the dominant's responsibility to care for you, so do not withhold this sort of information in an attempt at delicacy or humility.

If you are required to be the active partner in anal service, you should remember three keys to successful anal play:

1) Go slowly.

2) Use at least twice as much lubricant as you think you need.

3) Communicate.

Again, communication should be direct but respectful, especially since many people find the extreme intimacy of anal penetration makes them feel vulnerable. Describe your actions just before you do them: Master, I'm entering you slowly now, Master. (Note that some dominants will prefer you to refer to your penis as "theirs" to remind you that your body is their property: Master, I'm putting your cock inside you now, Master.) If you are using a dildo for penetration, you will need to communicate all the more, as you won't be able to feel resistance as readily.

If you think you may be called upon to service a dominant anally, be sure to read at least one of the titles suggested below and review safer sex procedures for anal sex.

Suggested Reading: Most general sex manuals will cover anal sex, but rarely in great detail. In addition to the title mentioned in the lesson on anal plugs, you may enjoy Bert Herman's <u>Trust: The Hand Book</u> as well as a newer title, <u>The Ultimate Guide to Anal Sex for Women</u> by Tristan Taormino.

Suggested Viewing: Nina Hartley's <u>Guide to Anal Sex</u>.

Body Servants: Ladies' Maids and Valets

Body servants are those responsible primarily for the physical care of their Owners. These are traditional roles, once considered among the most respectable and trusted positions in service. Because body servants work closely with their Owners, often in intimate settings like the bath or dressing room, they often enjoy the privileged role of confidant(e). These roles are also favorite subjects for BDSM erotica, as the personal nature of the lady's maid or valet suggests the possibility of sexual intimacy as well.

In modern household settings, where the number of servants is generally limited, the maid or valet may also perform services usually associated with the personal assistant or housekeeper or escort. In particular, the valet may double as a butler.

Lesson 30. Basic Personal Attendance

Review: Lessons on Obedience, Personal Care, and Positioning the Body. In these earlier lessons, you learned to take stock of your surroundings and to be aware of other people's presence and emotions. These are vitally important skills for all types of personal servants. You must learn to focus your attention on your Owner and to respond to his or her needs, even those that may remain unspoken.

The most fundamental type of service a maid* provides is what I refer to as fetch-and-carry. S/he will be expected to respond primarily to verbal commands (often answering verbally as well) by fetching items and conveying them to the Owner in a variety of postures. Of course, grace is paramount here. If the maid is slow or clumsy, s/he will not please.

Activity: To improve your posture, practice walking with a book balanced on your head. (If you plan to wear high heels for service, practice with them on.) When you feel comfortable with this exercise, try crawling with a large book

---

* For simplicity's sake, I refer throughout this section to "maids." The maid's role is one of the most popular in D/S arrangements, for both men and women, and so I have preferred the term here. I extend my apologies to the valets among my readers, a rarer but no less noble breed.

balanced on your back. (If you have knee or back problems that could be exacerbated by this posture, skip this activity.)

Activity: Procure a large tray (silver is lovely, but heavy). Practice carrying the tray – empty at first – and setting it down on a table until you can do so gracefully and with a minimum of noise. Then try carrying empty cups and saucers or glasses. Finally, fill the cups or glasses with water. Can you hold a laden tray with one hand while you distribute cups or glasses? (This will depend on the size and the weight of the tray, so do not be discouraged if you cannot manage with a full tray. The point is to know what you can and cannot handle.) Remember when lifting a heavy object to bend at the knees, not the waist, to avoid back strain; this is especially important if you are wearing heels.

Activity: Visit a busy restaurant and notice how the servers and bus boys handle plates. Practice some of these techniques at home.

Activity: Practice picking up and carrying small objects with your mouth. Try to avoid salivating on the object.

Activity: The curtsey is a very pretty skill for maids. To begin, stand erect. Step back with your right foot and bend down – your right knee with move toward your left foot. As you lower yourself, move your arms out to your sides. Keep your back straight and your head up. When you've bent as far as you can, bow your head gracefully for a heartbeat, then rise. Practice until you can perform the curtsey with fluid grace. In general, a full curtsey is reserved for when one is in evening wear (e.g. a floor-length skirt), so practice a shallower "bob" too.

The masculine equivalent is the bow. Bend forward from the hips approximately 20-45 degrees and nod your head slightly. Pause and rise. A shallower bow (from the waist) is less formal, but quicker and more practical for many occasions.

A helpful hint: Personal attendance is made much easier by excellent household organization. If you've made yourself familiar with the contents of the house, when Mistress asks you to fetch that old playbill from nineteen-ought-three, you'll know where to find it.

Further training: See the lesson for butlers for information on more advanced table service and the cooking chapter in the Household Management section for guides to tea service.

Suggested Reading: A Modern Man's Guide to Life, pp. 329-332. This section will provide a useful review of etiquette for maids and valets alike. For a slave, the hints are applicable regardless of the gender of the person you serve.

Suggested Viewing: The film Dangerous Liaisons – in particular the opening scenes – for a glimpse of the historical roles of man- and maid-servants.

Resources: Since balance is important to a maid, consider enrolling in ballet or yoga classes. Activities that build arm strength are also helpful.

Lesson 31. Voice-Training III: Verbal Response

An attractive speaking voice is a great asset in a maid. While sex slaves, for example, may only need the most basic voice-training skills, maids are often called upon to express opinions and may also need to engage in polite conversation from time to time. These skills become all the more important if the maid is undertaking other responsibilities, such as business affairs (personal assistant) or social outings (escort). This lesson will provide you with exercises to help improve your speech.

Activity: Record yourself having a conversation (set the recorder by the telephone, for example), or ask a friend to do so. (You may have to let the tape run for a while before you relax enough to speak naturally.)

Now, listen to the tape. Identify any verbal "tics" you may have. These may be meaningless filler phrases like "um" or "you know" or "like," or they may be habits like clearing your throat before speaking or laughing to distract from the harshness of a pointed statement.

It can be difficult to correct such habits, but it can be done. Try speaking more slowly. Before you open your mouth, mentally count to three and take a deep breath. Try to arrange your thoughts before you begin, as many tics are stalling devices to aid in "thinking on your feet." Ask a trusted friend to monitor your progress.

Resources: If you find this task overwhelming on your own, consider hiring a voice coach. These professionals often have a background in theater or speech pathology and can help you improve both the tone of your voice and your diction. They can sometimes help you modify a regional accent, too. General assertiveness training usually contains a voice coaching component as well.

Lesson 32. Uniforms for Maids

While all types of slaves may wear uniforms, it is the maid who is most closely identified with a particular style of dress: a short black dress with a frilly white apron and a small white cap. Fetish versions of this "French maid" outfit may include crinolines, seamed stockings, and high-heeled shoes and are readily available from lingerie shops like Frederick's of Hollywood.

What you wear when serving is primarily a matter of the Owner's taste and budget and your assigned tasks. Your uniform will be chosen to express your role and, to an extent, your personality. Ideally, you need a outfit that is proper but practical. Fetishwear, while lovely, should be reserved for special occasions – parties, teas, and the like – or for the bedroom. In all cases, uniforms should be clean and in good repair. The following exercises will help you determine your own needs and preferences in day-to-day uniforms.

Activity: Visit a hotel or other location where you will see professional maids at work. What tasks are they performing? What kinds of movements do they make: crouching, bending, reaching...? What kind of uniform, if any, do they wear?

Perhaps the most important reason for servants to wear a uniform is
that it sets them apart for special tasks and also serves to remind them of
their role. Even if a formal maid's uniform is beyond your means, you can
use other items to help remind you of your submission.

*Resources: The House of Uniforms (852 Lexington Ave. between 64th
and 65th Sts., New York, 1-888-707-3746, http://www.HouseofUniforms.com)
carries a wide selection of classic and modern apparel for maids and housekeepers. They ship world-wide. This is not a fetish boutique, so please be
discreet in your inquiries.*

Lesson 33. Cross-Dressing

The "sissy maid" – a cross-dressed male in service to a female – is a
staple of BDSM erotica. It is a role favored both by fetishistic cross-
dressers, who derive erotic gratification from being dressed in the clothing
of another gender, and by some seeking a safe way of exploring and
expressing their inner feminine selves. Women, too, may derive pleasure
and satisfaction from wearing men's clothing and serving as a valet or butler.

If cross-dressing interests you, it is important to ascertain the
source of your attraction to it. As I indicated above, cross-dressers usually

fall into one of several categories:

- fetishists or erotic cross-dressers;
- those who experience cross-dressing as humiliating;
- transformational cross-dressers.

If you are a fetishist, your primary interest in cross-dressing is erotic. You regularly find yourself sexually aroused when dressed, often by the feel of certain fabrics, like silk or velvet. Dressing may be part of your masturbation rituals. You don't necessarily feel less masculine (or feminine) when dressed.

Perhaps you find cross-dressing humiliating. If you are a butch woman who was forced to wear traditionally feminine clothing or an effeminate man who was made to act "like a real man" at some point in your life, you want to play out scenes that involve "forced" cross-dressing. The satisfaction you derive would come from experiencing feelings of shame about your dress. You may fantasize about being verbally humiliated about your appearance. You may also connect these feelings with submission or with sexual arousal.

If you are most interested in exploring the feminine (or masculine) components of your personality – in Jungian terms, your anima or animus – you may want to experiment with transformational cross-dressing. Here you dress to "pass" as another gender, masking those aspects of your appearance and behavior that express your usual gender presentation. You may be exploring your gender identity, or you may identify as transgendered.

While it is certainly possible to integrate any of these scenarios into your submission, they all pose certain challenges. If you are a fetishist, you may find it difficult to serve as a maid without the promise of some sexual play. You may want to consider training primarily as a sex slave, or including specific sexual techniques in your maid training. If you are determined to make domestic service and cross-dressing parts of your life, you must learn to control your sexual responses while dressed so that you can concentrate on your work.

If you enjoy humiliation, it may be very difficult for you to focus on work at all while dressed, as your emotions may run very high. You may also require a great deal of attention from the dominant in order to derive satisfaction from your experience. I would suggest that if you are capable of submission without dressing, you save dressing for special erotic "mind games" with the dominant, separate from day-to-day service.*

If you are a transformational cross-dresser, it is very possible to integrate your alternate persona into your maid service. Quite simply, while in service, you appear, and are treated as, the gender you wish to present. You will need to schedule your time carefully, since transformational cross-dressing can be a time-consuming activity, and you want to have sufficient time to accomplish your service tasks as well.

If you want to experiment with cross-dressing, try the following exercise.

Activity: Buy a pair of underpants of a type usually worn by another gender. These may be bikinis, briefs, or thongs for male slaves, or boxers, jock straps or briefs for women. Choose a fabric and style that you find pleasing. Wear the underpants under your regular street clothes. Record your feelings in your slave journal.

If you find you enjoy this exercise, you can expand it by wearing other garments – men's dress shirts and trousers or women's skirts and blouses. You may want to experiment with makeup or a false mustache. Write about your experiences and share them with your trainer.

Suggested Reading: Miss Vera's Finishing School for Boys Who Want to Be Girls *by Veronica Vera is a delightful must-read by the founder of the world's first cross-dressing academy. Miss Vera, herself a wonder to behold, will guide you step-by-step through the process of transformational cross-dressing. (See also Resources for more information on her school.)* Information for the Female to Male Cross Dresser and Transsexual *by Lou Sullivan provides helpful hints of use to female valets. See especially pp. 35-51.*

---

* *If you only feel submissive when dressed, but feel a need to be humiliated for this, I suggest that your needs might better be met by carefully constructed short-term BDSM scenes than in full-time service. Slavehood requires that you be able to put aside your immediate desires, including those for attention, positive or negative. Whatever the case, please spend some time exploring your overall feelings about submission before proceeding.*

Resources: If you are a male lady's maid, you might consider treating yourself to a few days in the able hands of Miss Veronica Vera (see suggested reading). Call (212) 242-6449 for a brochure and application. If you are unable to travel to her school in New York, you can also take advantage of prerecorded classes (1-900-884-VERA, $2.99/minute) and private tutorials with Miss Vera and her deans (1-900-288-VERA, $4.99/minute).

Lesson 34. Attending a Lady: The Maid

Among the most popular roles for submissives is the lady's maid. Ladies' maids may be of any gender, as, indeed, may be the ladies they serve. (The male "sissy maid" is a perennial favorite.) The maid role also has a devoted following among submissive fetishists, since it allows them to deal extensively with Mistress's wardrobe, and perhaps to wear a fetish-style uniform as well (see "Uniforms" above).

Traditionally, the realm of the maid was the bedroom and dressing room, where s/he was expected to help Madame with her toilette – clothing, makeup, and hair. S/he might also help in the bath. (BDSM erotica often moves the maid into the parlor to serve tea.) A maid would also accompany the Mistress wherever she traveled and might attend her while shopping. (Butlers might also be expected to perform these tasks.) Unlike some other slaves who appear in public – personal secretaries and escorts, for example – maids generally wear a uniform that sets them apart.

As a maid, you should learn as much as you can about a lady's toilette, both in theory and in practice. If you are working independently, you may choose to "serve yourself" for the time being.

Clothing

Activity: Inventory a wardrobe (your own or your trainer's). Make a comprehensive list of all the items of clothing, from underwear to outerwear. List colors, sizes, and types of fabric along with the style of garment: powder blue cashmere sweater set, size medium; 18 pairs black silk panties, size small. If you send clothing out to be laundered, this is an excellent opportunity to mark garments with a permanent laundry marker or to sew in name labels.

(Use initials and be sure to write where the ink will not be visible when the garment is being worn.) You may also want to weed out items that are no longer being worn for storage, sale, or to give away. Note also which items seem to be "old standbys" as these will give you the best sense of a person's preferred style.

Activity: Organize the wardrobe. You may want to see about adding an extra bar in the closet or buying some shelves for sweaters. Group the clothing by use (casual, formal, sport) and then by length, separating short sleeves from long sleeves, and perhaps, light colors from dark. Try to store any accessories, like scarves, with the garments they match: hang scarves on the hanger with dresses and blouses.

Now organize any shoes. If there are some that are worn only infrequently, store them in boxes, and tape a Polaroid picture of the pair to the end of the box for easy identification.

Activity: Practice setting out complete outfits, including jewelry (necklaces and bracelets can be hung over the hanger). Are there new combinations you might not have tried before?

It is important to get a sense of your Owner's style, particularly if you will be attending her as she shops. She may ask you for suggestions or opinions on garments, and if you are aware of her tastes, you will be in a better position to advise her. Familiarize yourself with her favorite shops. Does she read any fashion magazines? What public figures does she admire? Notice when she comments on another woman's dress: what does she find attractive? Tacky? If you are working independently, try to determine what your own taste says about you. Are you a classic dresser? Sporty? Provocative?

Suggested Reading: Work Clothes: Casual Dress for Serious Work by Kim Johnson Gross, et al. covers men's and women's attire. Lucy's List by Lucy D. Curtis contains shopping tips for women who wear larger sizes. Elsa Klensch's Style is a basic guide to women's fashions and accessories.

Makeup and Hair

In addition to clothing, maids must be familiar with skin care and makeup. If you are a woman yourself, you may already be comfortable with makeup techniques. Review your own responses to the "Personal Care for Slaves" lesson to get a sense of how you relate to "beauty culture."

Activity: Take a class in makeup and skin care. Local beauty colleges and department stores often offer "makeover" classes.

Activity: Get a makeover at a cosmetic counter or visit a spa for a facial. Notice both what tools the aesthetician uses and her way of touching the skin.

Activity: Make a point of reading some of the more popular fashion and beauty magazines to get a sense of both classic makeup techniques and the current styles. **Elle** and **Vogue** have regular makeup columns and **Allure** is devoted to personal care alone (as opposed to fashion).

Finally, some maids are asked to style their Mistress's hair. While some styles require a good deal of skill, others need only a little practice. Again, fashion and beauty magazines are a good source of information and ideas.

Suggested Reading: <u>Making Faces</u> by Kevyn Aucoin, <u>Women's Face: Skin Care and Makeup</u> by Kim Johnson Gross, et al., <u>Ultimate Makeup & Beauty</u> by Mary Quant, <u>Hair: A Book of Braiding and Styles</u> by Anne Akers Johnson, <u>Haircutting at Home</u> by John R. Albano.

Lesson 35. Attending a Gentleman: The Valet

The valet (traditionally pronounced in English with the emphasis on the first syllable and a hard "t" at the end) is the masculine equivalent of the lady's maid. Also called a manservant, "gentleman's gentleman" or simply so-and-so's "man," the valet assists in a gentleman's toilette and may often fulfill other functions, such as light cleaning and cooking, correspondence and errands, or driving. He may also escort a gentleman on his travels.

Clothing

In general, a man's toilette is much simpler than a woman's. Aside from simple matters of grooming, many of which will be taken care of by the man's barber, men need only make sure that they and their clothing are clean and tidy. It is the valet's job to assure that all clothing is properly looked after and, often, to assemble outfits for the gentleman to don.

Activity: See the Clothing Inventory exercise in Lesson 31.

Men's fashion, particularly in business and formal dress, changes much more slowly and subtly than women's. Barring any radical changes in his size, a man can expect to wear a conservative, well-constructed suit for years, not just a season or two. Also the difference in quality between a well-made suit and a shoddy one is vast, whereas women are often shocked to discover that expensive designer clothes hold up no better than their mid-range counterparts. Since a decent suit will set a gentleman back at least $500, valets are most often charged with caring for suits and other expensive garments. A valet-in-training will need to learn as much as possible about men's clothing.

Activity: Visit an upscale clothier. Examine – and, if possible, try on – some well-made suits. (See the suggested reading for tips on how to distinguish a good suit from one that is merely expensive.) Engage the salesperson in conversation about the differences between styles and brands of suits.

Most suits require dry cleaning – the well-dressed man shuns "wash and wear" suits – but the cleaning process can quickly weaken the fabric's fibers and age the suit prematurely. Instead, brush the suit and steam out any wrinkles. Suits should only be cleaned when they have visible stains or if airing does not remove the smell of tobacco or body odors.

*Suggested Reading: Clothes and the Man: the Principles of Fine Men's
Dress and Style and the Man by Alan Flusser are the two best introductions to
the fine art of dressing a man well. Paisley Goes with Nothing by Hal Rubenstein with Jim Mullen, a more recent title, provides humorous but sound
advice on matters of style as well as the social graces. Work Clothes: Casual
Dress for Serious Work by Kim Johnson Gross, et al., covers men's and women's
attire for "casual Fridays" and beyond. Color for Men, by Carole Jackson
with Kalia Lulow, applies the four-season color principles to men's dress.*

Leather Care: Shoes, Boots, and Accessories

Dress shoes and boots often rival suits for the position of most
expensive item in a man's wardrobe, and like suits, leather shoes are
expected to last for years with proper care. Studies have shown that in a
traditional business environment, mussed hair and even a threadbare jacket
can be overlooked, but down-at-the-heels shoes make a singularly bad
impression. The solution: regular polishing.

Valets with a military background will have a distinct advantage here,
but it is important to remember that fine, thin leather should be treated
with more care than the thicker leather used to make combat boots. Boots
can be polished with a waxy paste polish for a high gloss, but men's dress
shoes should be treated to a high-quality cream polish.

Remove the laces, then wipe the shoe with a clean cotton cloth to
remove any surface dirt or dust. Apply a thin coat of polish and let it dry.
Use a brush to remove the bulk of the polish (be sure to get any polish
out of the lace holes and indentations in wing tips), then buff with a soft
cloth. Use liquid edge dressing to blacken the sides of the soles, right
below the uppers, if needed.

Cowboy boots should be treated like fine shoes, unless they are made of an unusual material, like snake or alligator, in which case you should check with the manufacturer about cleaning procedures. Be sure to match polish colors carefully.

Many work, engineer, and motorcycle boots have a oily surface that isn't really meant to take a shine. In fact, if you use saddle soap, you can remove this water resistant coating and render the boot useless in damp conditions. Instead, use a brush to remove any caked-on dirt, and wipe the boot with a damp cloth as needed. Some boots can be treated with a leather conditioner like Lexol. Again, it is best to check with the individual manufacturer.

Leather accessories like wallets and belts can be cleaned with a very small amount of cream polish in a matching color.

Suggested Reading: <u>Leather and Latex Care: How to Keep Your Leather and Latex Looking Great</u> by Kelly J. Thibault is the single best guide to caring for dress and fetish leathers.

The Gentleman's Gentleman: Public Services for the Private Man

If you're familiar with Jeeves, the cool, collected, and very correct manservant to Bertie Wooster in P. G. Wodehouse's frothy comic novels, then you will know that a valet will often have more on his hands than shoe polish. Jeeves – definitely the brains in the Wooster operation – routinely handles both mundane affairs, like luncheons and shopping, for his hapless master, while effortlessly averting social disasters.

While most valets don't face the challenges that Jeeves does – most masters being better endowed in gray matter than old Bertie W. – you should be prepared to deal with minor matters of household organizing and basic secretarial duties.

Activity: Read one of Wodehouse's Jeeves novels: <u>Life with Jeeves</u>, published by Penguin, is an omnibus edition including <u>Right Ho, Jeeves</u>, <u>The Inimitable Jeeves</u>, and <u>Very Good, Jeeves</u>. Make a list of all the tasks that Jeeves is charged with in the space of one novel. (You needn't include all the comedy-of-errors plots, just the domestic and secretarial tasks.) Then read the appropriate lessons in this book if you don't yet feel equal to the tasks described.

Suggested Reading: For a well-rounded sense of the tradition of the manservant, the Lord Peter Wimsey mysteries of Dorothy Sayers are as indispensable as Wodehouse's novels. See also the titles suggested in the lesson on Butlers.

Lesson 36. The Personal Secretary

Before "longtime companions" and "significant others," the term "personal secretary" was a euphemism for "lover." Although officially society did not condone non-marital relationships, polite company acknowledged the (often young and attractive) men and women who shared their famous lovers' lives with this sobriquet. Often the person in question was more of an escort than a secretary, but sometimes they did indeed attend to their partner's papers and business calls.

Why would someone with considerable business skills choose the life of a slave over the life of a capitalist? For the same reason that other educated, upwardly mobile people might choose to spend their time dressed as French maids or butlers: they enjoy being of service to another person.

In fact, the role of personal secretary is ideal for people who need to earn an income, but prefer to work at home, or whose dominant companion runs a business and needs help. (Think of the many "mom and pop" businesses, run by husband-and-wife teams, for example.) Personal secretaries may want to keep their professional skills up to par, or may simply prefer working in a professional setting rather than in household service. Dominants who work as writers or artists often appreciate help with the business side of their careers, so they have more freedom to create. In any case, this sometimes overlooked submissive role, when executed with care, provides a wonderful alternative to the more traditional maid- or man-servant or sex slave roles.

The bywords of personal assistants are Efficiency and Discretion. Since the dominant's livelihood may in part depend on your performance, you will be expected to act in a professional manner when on the job. While in the office (or on the phone) you are Mr. Jones' assistant, at least as far as his clients or customers are concerned. You must take care not to allow any emotions to interfere with your job performance. (See "Business Ethics and Slavehood" for more on this topic.)

Highly organized and able slaves – who are well-suited to the personal secretary role – may have a difficult time maintaining an appropriate sense of submission while working. There is no contradiction between being competent and being of service, as the many business-persons who would be utterly lost without their secretaries will tell you. Just as a housekeeper must be respectful and friendly with suppliers but submissive to his or her Owner, a personal secretary can project an air of confident professionalism to clients, while showing deference to the Owner.

Exercise: Write or re-work your résumé as if you were applying to be a dominant's personal secretary. What special categories of information might you include? What skills would you emphasize? What skills might you hope to gain?

Suggested Reading: The Professional Secretary's Handbook (3rd ed.) and The Professional Secretary's Management Skills by John Spencer and Adrian Pruss are excellent guides to business etiquette and protocol.

Telephone Etiquette

Miss Abernathy notes with dismay the decline of proper telephone etiquette, both in the public and private arenas. As a personal secretary, you will often need to make business (and perhaps personal) calls for the dominant. Please remember that your tone and style of presentation on the telephone reflect on the dominant.

Activity: When you make calls for yourself, practice these steps. (If you are calling a shop for information only, you can even pretend to be calling on behalf of someone else.)

1) Always identify yourself with your full name. (Unfortunately, these days you can no longer expect the person on the other end of the line to return the favor, although in most circumstances, they should.)

2) Mention that you are calling on behalf of Mr./Ms. X (the dominant) if this information is relevant. (It will be, for example, if you are making reservations at a restaurant.)

3) State the purpose of your call as simply and directly as possible: This is John Smith. I'm calling on behalf of Mr. Brown, who is a patient of Dr. Lowry's. Mr. Brown would like to make an appointment with the doctor for next Thursday.

4) When leaving a message on an answering machine or voicemail, spell your name and repeat your phone number (and area code, if necessary) twice. Speak slowly and clearly, over-pronouncing numbers.

5) Avoid casual language: "yeah" and "hey" have no place in a business call, particularly if you are not personally acquainted with the speaker. Never say "hunh?" or "what?" if you haven't heard something clearly. The latter can sound too curt and the former, Neanderthal. Say "Would you repeat that please?" or "What did you say, please?" instead. Never use profanity, even if you are angry or the other party has used it first. (If faced with an angry caller, it is professional to react with even more formality, not less.)

6) If you have received help from someone who has not identified him- or herself by name, it is appropriate to ask, "With whom am I speaking, please?" Then thank the person for their help, using their name: Thank you, Lisa, I appreciate your help today.

Writing Letters

After telephoning, the most common task for personal secretaries is letter-writing. The personal letter is a dying art, and the business letter is often mired in mumbo-jumbo and cliché.

Be as clear and direct as possible, while avoiding unnecessary information that may confuse the reader. Check the letter carefully for grammar and spelling errors, and refer to a standard secretarial manual if you are in doubt about forms of address or style.

Exercise: Write a business-style letter requesting information on a product
or service you have seen advertised in the newspaper.

Exercise: Write a formal thank-you note for a gift you have recently received.
(Consider writing a thank-you note to your trainer!)

Newer technologies, like email, have changed business writing styles
dramatically. Some things remain consistent, however. An electronic
medium does not give the user the right to ignore common courtesy; in
fact, it requires knowledge of a special set of social graces sometimes
referred to as "netiquette." Particularly when corresponding by email for
business, observe the standard form of the business letter as closely as
possible: use standard spelling, capitalization, and punctuation; end with
your full name, title, and company name; and provide an email address to
which the recipient of your mail can respond. Finally, you should be aware
that commercial messages are unwelcome on most newsgroups, mailing
lists, and bulletin boards.

*Suggested Reading: If your handwriting could stand some improvement,
you may benefit from* Write Now *by Getty and Dubay and* Teach Yourself
Better Handwriting *by Sassoon and Briem.* How to Write First-Class Letters
by L. Sue Baugh, The Art of Letter Writing *by Lassor A. Blumenthal, and*
Lifetime Encyclopedia of Letters *by Harold E. Meyer, revised and expanded
edition, are all helpful guides to correspondence.*

Office Organization

In some ways, managing an office is not unlike managing a house.
Your success depends on your ability to plan ahead, minimize waste, and
maximize productivity while maintaining a comfortable, pleasant
environment for all.

If you have enough storage space, try to buy office supplies in bulk;
you'll almost always save money.

Activity: Review the process for creating a Master Grocery List in the Household Management section of this book. Now create an Master Supply List for your office. (See the suggested reading for some hints.) Then, following the instructions in the lesson for Housekeepers, create a Price Book for office supplies. Compare prices both at a small local stationery store and at an office supply superstore.

Suggested Reading: Organizing Your Home Office for Success by Lisa Kanarek is the single best title on this topic. It covers everything from home office design to filing systems.

Time Management

To keep your work on track, you'll need to use "To Do" lists. A simple wall calendar with sufficient space to write (for long-range planning) and a loose-leaf binder filled with 8 1/2 x 11 paper are all you really need.

Activity: On your wall calendar, enter due dates and appointments: June 12: Balliwick project due; June 13: Mr. Jones haircut, 3 p.m. You can also use a large appointment book, but be sure that it allows you to see at least one month at a time.

Activity: For your daily "To Do" list, follow these steps.

1) Label a blank sheet of paper with the date.

2) Check the calendar to see if there are any deadlines or appointments. Write them at the top of the page.

3) Next, check to see what projects may be due in 1, 2, 3, and 4 weeks. These will, in all likelihood, form the basis of your tasks for the day, with projects due in one week commanding more attention than projects due later.

4) Now write down the specific tasks you want to get done: type Balliwick letter, phone accountant, reconfirm flight reservations... Try to group similar activities together: make all your phone calls at one time, when possible.

5) Prioritize your tasks by numbering them from most pressing to least pressing. (You will also want to identify which tasks may not need attention at all: Some problems simply resolve themselves with time.)

6) Begin with the most pressing task and work steadily through your list.

You may prefer to use a commercial personal planning system. These can be very helpful, but keep in mind that they should make your work easier, not more difficult. If you find you spend more time fussing with your planner than working, find a simpler system. The suggested reading will help you create one that works for you. Of course, you will also need to consider the dominant's work style and planning needs, too. Find out if s/he prefers a specific system and try to work with that.

Business Ethics and Slavehood

Undoubtedly you've heard the old adage that forbids mixing business and pleasure. But a slave who works in his or her Owner's business is doing just that. How can you maintain a solid working relationship while acknowledging your respective roles in each other's lives?

The answer should by now be familiar: communicate. When you are making your preliminary arrangement for a slave contract, spell out the boundaries between work and play, between public and private, in detail. Whatever makes you feel efficient and competent, you should have in this case. It may be a simple change in modes of address: you call her "Mistress" in the house, but "Ms. Jones" in the office, and she calls you "slave" after hours, but "Miss Smith" at work. The titles signal a temporary change of role in response to the new, more public setting.

If you have been trained not to speak unless spoken to, you may have to arrange a sign, if only for yourself, that allows you to speak more freely in the office. Perhaps you can arrange a ritual with the Owner in which he places his hand over your mouth and then removes it, saying, "Speak at will, until I tell you otherwise." Even something so simple, an acknowledgment of your special relationship, can help you make the transition from slave to secretary.

With more and more home-based businesses and telecommuters, the lines between business and pleasure are being blurred. With some communication, you can avoid the pitfalls of the office romance while maintaining your sense of submission.

Exercise: Devise a ritual that you think would help you make the transition from private to public more smoothly. If appropriate, share this ritual with your trainer, or keep a copy in your slave journal.

Further training: See the lessons on Escorts and Butlers.

Suggested Reading: Although it is addressed primarily to aspiring executives in traditional work environments, Molloy's Live for Success contains some useful observations on the unspoken rules of corporate culture. It will be helpful if you are doing business in a conservative field.

Resources: Your local business college, vocational training center, or community college no doubt offers a wide range of courses to improve your clerical and general secretarial skills.

HOUSE SERVANTS

House servants are distinguished from personal servants and assistants by the focus of their work. As the name suggests, house servants are primarily charged with the running of a house and do not generally attend specific individuals. Of course, in contemporary settings, most slaves will be serving an individual in a small household, not running an English country manor, so the duties outlined in this section may well be combined with the responsibilities of a personal servant for many. Still, Miss Abernathy believes it is useful for slaves-in-training to have a sense of the more traditional posts, should they ever find themselves in service in a larger household.

House servants will have varying degrees of contact with people outside the household, but, like personal secretaries and escorts, they should be familiar with the norms of the society in which their Owner moves. The reading list for this section suggests some classic etiquette manuals which may be of use to you.

Suggested Reading: Emily Post's Etiquette by Peggy Post (16th edition). Miss Manners' Guide to Excruciatingly Correct Behavior and the Miss Manners' Basic Training Series by Judith Martin. Those in management positions, like some housekeepers and butlers, will want to avail themselves of People Skills by Robert Bolton.

Lesson 37. The Housekeeper

Housekeepers, like butlers, are primarily household managers, and as such, are responsible both for their own work and that of others. Even if you are the only slave in the house, you may be expected to supervise repair people and other workers who come to the house periodically. You will also be the "public face" of the household for suppliers like grocers or delivery people. If there are other staff members (slaves or employees), it may be your job to train them or at least to inform them of the specific needs of the Owner and the household. You will also be the person in charge of household shopping.

This last point brings us to the basic distinction between a housekeeper and, say, a houseboy. The houseboy is a factotum, there to do what needs to be done. As such s/he is responsible for completing the assigned task to the best of his or her ability, but is not concerned with the "big picture" of the running of the household. The housekeeper, on the other hand, while not necessarily immediately responsible for the minutiae of individual tasks, must always keep in mind the best interests of the household as a whole. Traditionally, the housekeeper answered only to the butler, who in turn answered directly to the householder.

In practical terms, this means that housekeepers are generally entrusted with some financial responsibility. As the "keeper of the keys," they regulate household expenditures on a day-to-day basis, according to a budget set by the Owner. Their role also draws together all aspects of housecleaning, as well as the managerial responsibilities mentioned above. The present lesson will cover these three areas: housekeeping, budgeting, and handling of other servants and suppliers.

Home Economics and Responsible Housekeeping

In a contemporary dominant/submissive household, the house-keeper may well be the one performing all the cleaning tasks without assistance. You will need to organize your time and your tools carefully to accomplish everything.

Exercise: For one week, keep track of the amount of time you spend on the following activities: cleaning, cooking, shopping, and other household chores. Based on this information, create a weekly household schedule for yourself. (Be sure to review the Household Management section of this book, and refer to a standard maintenance housecleaning schedule in one of the suggested reading titles.) Don't forget to include travel time to stores, laundries, or other frequent destinations, like video rental stores or the public library.

Looking at a standard schedule, note any tasks that you might not be able to accomplish by yourself: washing upper-story windows or shampooing the carpets, for example. Phone several cleaning services and ask for price quotes for these jobs. (Don't hesitate to ask for references from any cleaning service and to follow up on them.) Finally, make a list of these tasks (and approximate expense) to present to the Owner with a request to hire outside help.

Now you will be ready to tackle those tasks that remain. Be sure you have the necessary tools before you start, and work methodically, finishing one task before you start the next.

A note is in order here about environmentally responsible housecleaning. While Madison Avenue would like us to believe that we need dozens of different cleaning products to make our floors sparkle and our toilet bowls gleam, in fact most of these products are at best unnecessary and at worst dangerous. "Green" housecleaning recommends itself in many ways: it is safer for the person cleaning; it protects our natural environment; the products used are much less likely to cause allergic reactions, making the house more pleasant for residents and guests alike; and, of special interest to the economy-minded slave, green products are more versatile and significantly less expensive. A quart of white vinegar and a box of baking soda will clean 90% of the house for under $2. And, yes, they really work.

In addition to cleaning, housekeepers may also be called upon to organize items in the house. It seems every house has a dreaded junk closet where all the memorabilia and useless impulse purchases of a lifetime collect. Organizing these closets, indeed a daunting task, does not excite most people, and so they become a pet project for dominants to assign to slaves. Before you begin, you must get clear instructions from the dominant regarding the contents of the area to be organized. May you dispose of twenty-year-old laundry lists and grocery receipts? Will the dominant consider selling or donating to charity clothing that s/he hasn't worn in a decade and will, in all honesty, never fit into again? (Kindly don't mention that last bit!) What about the juicer, home exercise machine, and LPs that haven't seen the light of day since Jimmy Carter was president? It may help to make a complete list of the dubious items and present it to the dominant, along with the names of good consignment shops and worthy charities in your area.

Activity: Clean your own Dreaded Junk Closet. If you find it difficult to get rid of old, admittedly useless items that you nonetheless are passionately, irrationally attached to, put them in a box. Mark the box with today's date and put it back in the closet. If you haven't missed the items in 6 months, give the box away. Unopened.

Suggested Reading: The Complete Home Organizer by Maxine Ordesky, The Cleaning Encyclopedia by Don Aslett. Please also note the titles suggested in the introduction to the household management section. They will stand you in good stead. Also strongly recommended are two titles by Annie Berthold-Bond, Clean & Green and The Green Kitchen Handbook, both of which are essential reading for the environmentally responsible housekeeper.

Budgeting

Perhaps the most difficult responsibility of the housekeeper – and the one that makes him or her indispensable – is budgeting. By entrusting you with finances, the dominant is honoring you with greater responsibility, which should awaken in you a sense of humility and gratitude.

Dominants will make different arrangements for household funds according to their circumstances. Some may give you a certain amount of cash weekly or monthly to cover household expenses. If this is the case, be sure to keep the money separate from any personal funds you may have, and never borrow from household funds to pay for personal expenses. Alternatively, the dominant may choose to establish a bank account specifically for household expenses and will then furnish you with an ATM or debit card. Still others may want you to pay for purchases with a charge or credit card and will pay the bill monthly. In any case, the dominant should provide you with some petty cash for bus fare, parking meters, and the like.

For our purposes here, we will limit ourselves to a discussion of grocery budgeting, since this is the most common task assigned to housekeepers. The general principles apply to almost any type of household budgeting, however.

Activity: Refer to your Master Shopping List (see Lesson 19). Using a piece of lined or graph paper, create four columns. In the far left-hand column, write the names of the items on your Master Shopping List. (Remember to specify brand names and package sizes, where applicable.) At the top of the remaining columns write the names of supermarkets, starting with your regular market and including, if possible, one bulk or discount store (this may be a members-only or co-op store; if so, note the membership price, too).

Now visit each of the stores and note the prices of the items on your Master List.* If a given store doesn't carry your usual brand or has an unusual size, note that too. The resulting list is your Price Book.

When you are preparing to shop for a given item, check your Price Book. Does one store carry paper products at a discount? Try to visit that store when you're in the neighborhood and stock up. In figuring savings, you'll also want to consider the distance you have to travel to get to a store and any other potential expenses (like membership fees).

Update your Price Book every other month or so. Often you can do so by checking your itemized register receipts or printed advertisements.

You will also want to get into the habit of clipping coupons and using them. Some people have a curious aversion to coupons, but they can save the budget-minded slave a great deal of money. In most places, grocery stores regularly send out flyers to area residents, and Sunday newspapers often seem to contain more advertisements than news. Both are good sources of coupons. When you clip a coupon, note the amount and expiration date on your weekly shopping list next to the appropriate item. Attach the coupons you intend to use immediately to the list and file the others in an envelope. As you are completing your weekly shopping list, check this file for items you may have forgotten. You should also use this opportunity to weed out any expired coupons. If you see that

* You may need to be subtle about this task. I know of a number of people who, when noting down prices, have been accosted by suspicious store managers. Apparently the managers believed these people were "spies" from rival stores trying to undercut their prices. In one case, no amount of explaining would calm the manager. If you encounter this kind of resistance, I suggest you cross the store off your list and choose another.

certain stores regularly provide coupons for a given item, note this fact in your Price Book.

Beyond buying at good prices, housekeepers are expected to make the best use of the items they do buy. One way to avoid food waste is to draw up weekly menus and shop accordingly. The general principle here is to minimize waste by incorporating leftovers into other meals.

So, for example, if you are serving a roast chicken on Monday night, you can buy one slightly larger than necessary and use the leftover meat to make chicken salad for lunch on Tuesday. The bones can then be used to make stock for soup served as a first course on Thursday night. Leftover vegetables can be used in soups or quiches, and fruits can be cut up for salads, baked into pies, tortes, and muffins, or stewed into compote or a flavorful ice cream topping. Day-old French or Italian bread can be used for croutons or seasoned for bread crumbs.

Exercise: Draw up a weekly menu that incorporates leftovers. Use this menu in conjunction with your Master Grocery List to plan your shopping.

Suggested Reading: The Budget Kit (Second Edition) by Judy Lawrence.

Handling Other Servants and Suppliers

As I noted at the beginning of this lesson, housekeepers are traditionally household managers. As such, you may be expected to hire or supervise other workers in the house, including, perhaps, other less experienced slaves.

In all cases, it is important for you to be clear, direct, and firm about your requirements. Try to get any price quotes in writing, and reconfirm the date and time of any appointment by phone. If you are hiring a worker from an agency, ask for a list of previous clients and call a few. If you are hiring a self-employed person, ask for references and request a copy of their licensing numbers, if appropriate. If you do so in a businesslike manner, without apology, you will not offend professionals.

Try to cultivate good relationships with suppliers and others you do business with regularly. Ask their names and use them in your conversation. It is sometimes appropriate to tip delivery people; check a good etiquette guide for specifics and note the amounts in the back of your Price Book or a household journal. Do not be afraid to encourage a healthy competition between suppliers: If you can get a better price elsewhere, say so. Other suppliers may be willing to match the price. In all cases, be courteous and friendly.

Resources: Starkey International Institute provides eight-week courses in Household Management covering service management, personal dynamics, culinary arts, and household service skills. Their offices are located at 1350 Logan St., Denver, CO 80203 and they can be reached at http:// www.starkeyintl.com/ or by phone at (303) 832-5510. Please note that Starkey offers training and job placement for professional domestic servants, so be discreet in your inquiries.

Lesson 38. The Butler

Review: All the previous material, especially the sections on household management, personal servants, and housekeepers.

As an introduction to the role of butler, it may be useful to spend a few moments investigating the meaning of the word itself, and its relation to some other common terms. What distinguishes a butler from a steward or a majordomo? All of these terms refer, generally, to servants working at a managerial level. Usually they serve in large households or estates, and they have traditionally been male, although recent years have seen an increase in the number of women training as professional butlers.

The term "butler" derives from the French for "bottle bearer" and originally referred to the servant in charge of wine and liquor. Later this role was expanded, until the butler came to head up the household staff. (Nannies and governesses, notably, did not fall under his command.) Butlers will receive guests at the door, direct the serving of meals at table, and often provide any number of personal services as well. The butler usually answers only to the master of the house.

A "steward" – the heir of the medieval seneschal – is distinguished from a butler by the fact that his responsibilities may extend beyond the house itself to the grounds. Whereas butlers supervise only domestic staff, stewards may deal with gardeners, stable masters, and other servants on a large estate property. If there are tenants on the land, such as farmers or craftspeople, he will collect their rent and oversee their accounts.

A "majordomo" fills a role similar to that of a steward, and the titles are sometimes used interchangeably. The term is also sometimes used to refer to a valet or butler whose job description needs to be more flexible, including, for instance, supervision of building projects, business interests, or other more specialized tasks.

Most Americans, unless they belong to the wealthiest of the upper classes, have never seen a "real" (i.e., English) butler, but the popular media will have given them a clear image of one: an older, rather distinguished gentleman in a dark suit, striped waistcoat, and bow tie who greets guests solemnly at the door and conducts them through dark, paneled rooms to the Master's library. Formerly, butlers had a reputation for being snobbish, ready to raise an eyebrow or purse disapproving lips at the slightest departure from the rules of upper class etiquette. Indeed, many butlers were far better educated than the other servants (and probably many of the guests), might have traveled extensively, and had spent their lives in splendid surroundings to which they had undoubtedly grown accustomed. Needless to say, a superior attitude is not becoming to a slave, and even professional butlers are now strongly discouraged from appearing to be anything but humbly helpful.

Exercise: Write a short paragraph about butlers and their responsibilities, based either on your observation of a professional butler or on stories, films, or television shows you have seen.

Suggested Reading: See the titles listed in the lesson on Attending a Gentleman. In addition, A Butler's Life: Scenes from the Other Side of the Silver Salver by Christopher Allen and Kimberly Burton Allen is mandatory – and entertaining – reading.

Suggested Viewing: Remains of the Day, based on the novel by Kazuo Ishiguro, is a touching drama that centers on the moral dilemmas of an aging English butler.

Decorum

The butler must be a master (if you will pardon the term) of decorum, knowing what is proper for every occasion and under any circumstance. Of all the submissive roles, this one requires the most intense study and preparation.

Activity: Procure a copy of a standard etiquette manual, such as Emily Post's Etiquette, and read it cover-to-cover. Yes, some of it may be tedious, but you may be surprised to find that, as a butler, others will turn to you for advice on the niceties of social interactions. If you don't know the answer to a question, make a point of finding out.

Like maids, butlers are often associated with a specific uniform, in this case, the dark suit. By wearing a suit – often with a striped waistcoat – and being addressed by his surname, the butler displayed his high rank among the domestic servants. While you may certainly wear other clothing as appropriate for your various tasks, a conservative, well-cut dark suit – sometimes formal evening wear – is expected for formal service. (Professional butlers-in-training are required to wear an immaculate suit, shirt, and tie at all times.)

You should also carefully review the material on Forms of Address, as you will be expected to speak more formally than most other slaves. The male and female heads of the household are "Sir" and "Madame," as are any guests. Day servants may be addressed as "Mr.," "Mrs.," "Ms.," or "Miss" and their surname, at least in the presence of Sir or Madame. You can expect to be addressed by your surname alone. (More casual households may allow for the use of first names.)

Perhaps the most challenging aspect of decorous behavior is knowing when to eschew the rules. The guidelines for breaking rules of etiquette are as follows:

1) "The rules of etiquette may, within reasonable limits, be waived if observing them would cause distress to those unaware of such rules.

2) "The ostentatious observation of simple rules of etiquette is rude."*

Exercise: In your slave journal, write about a time when you felt "out of your element" and intimidated. It may have been while traveling in a foreign country or at a formal event, like a wedding, where you knew almost no one. How did you respond to the situation? What aspects of the situation are most prominent in your memory: unfamiliar manners, perhaps, or being unable to communicate with others? What might have made you feel more comfortable?

Remember that, while you know yourself to be submissive, others may find the simple presence of a butler intimidating. By being unobtrusively helpful, rather than overbearingly formal, you will put those around you at their ease.

The Butler's Book

Have you ever known someone who invites you to dinner many times without ever serving the same dish or wine twice? Who remembers that you hate lima beans and are allergic to tomatoes? Who asks about your Great Aunt Mathilda's hip surgery and remembers the names of every one of your seven cats? They may have a photographic memory... or they may know the secret of the Butler's Book.

In the business world, it has long been the duty of secretaries to keep track of personal details and to brief their employer before business lunches and cocktail parties. In the domestic world, this is the butler's realm. Quite simply, the butler takes note of everything and documents it in a notebook, or, more recently, on a computer.

For example, when you are organizing a dinner party, you might note who attended, what dishes were served, what the host and/or hostess wore, what flowers were on the table, who preferred which beverages (and who drank no alcohol), who did not touch the salad, and so on. The butler must of course be a model of discretion, but it is always helpful to note

---

* *Modern Man's Guide to Life, p. 355.*

down any personal details that guests mention: upcoming anniversaries or birthdays, new business ventures, religious affiliations (and any relevant dietary restrictions), the names of partners or spouses, children, pets, and (perhaps especially) sworn enemies or disgruntled ex-lovers.

The Butler's Book is also the place to record the names and numbers of catering services, dry cleaners, tailors, florists, gardeners, and other services that the household uses regularly. Include the name of the owner of the business or your contact person and any special prices or discounts you've received in the past.

Activity: Create a Butler's Book for your household. For more guidance, see Cassandra Kent's Household Hints & Tips, p. 9 or the sample on page 155 of A Butler's Life.

Lesson 39. Advanced Butlering

A butler's work is never done, and it is not unusual for professionals to work sixty- or even eighty-hour weeks during busy seasons. The range of skills an accomplished butler can possess is truly staggering: among the technical skills listed in one butlering school's catalog are care and handling of antiques, bed-making, afternoon tea service, caddy assembly, car care, pet care, clothes and packing, care of fine art objects, CPR training, international etiquette and protocol, care of fine linens, fire protection, flower arranging, haute couture, home security, ironing and steaming, laundry, leather and shoe polishing, liquor and bar set up, care of oriental rugs, dealing with rental services, emergency sewing and repair, silver polishing, table setting, tray service, tree and landscape care, and wines... to name just a few.

Of course, no slave-in-training is expected to come fully equipped with all of these skills. If s/he did, what would be left for the trainer? You will notice that some of these skills have been covered in other lessons (clothes and packing, laundry, tray service) and some you may already possess as a result of your life experiences (pet care, dealing with rental services, CPR training). That being the case, we will focus in this lesson on some of the special skills for which butlers are best known, and which constitute the most helpful types of service to busy dominants: serving houseguests and planning parties.

Attending Houseguests

While butlers are essentially domestic servants, they are often called upon to interact with guests. Whether the guest is visiting for an evening or for a month, s/he becomes your responsibility for the duration.

Even if you suspect that a guest may be sharing the Owner's quarters during his or her stay, prepare a separate bedroom, which should be as comfortably appointed as possible. The following items are essential: clean cotton sheets, extra pillows and blankets in a variety of weights, a bed board for those needing an extra-firm mattress, a good reading lamp, several water glasses, a variety of current general interest periodicals, a daily newspaper, an ashtray and matches (if smoking is permitted in the house), a full box of tissues, an alarm clock, a radio, ear plugs, an eye mask (for sleeping), plenty of good-quality wood hangers, and a selection of safer sex supplies, including a stack of clean white hand towels. If there is no outlet near the bed, place an extension cord in the drawer of a bedside table. Fresh towels should be provided daily, and the bathroom should be stocked with basic toiletries, including a new toothbrush, a selection of soaps (both scented and unscented), shampoo, unscented body and hand lotion, women's sanitary supplies, aspirin, and a non-aspirin pain reliever like Tylenol or Motrin. An oversize robe or kimono is a lovely touch.

You may be asked to unpack a visitor's bags. Hang clothing in the closet and place undergarments neatly in drawers. Medications should be placed at bedside along with a water glass, while makeup and toiletries may be stowed in the guest bathroom. Any personal items, including sex toys or SM gear, should be placed discreetly in the bedside table or in the closet.

If the guests include a slave, inquire in advance about sleeping arrangements. You may need to provide a futon or cot for the slave.

Beds should be made after the guest rises and should be turned down immediately after dinner. It is unnecessary to change the sheets each night unless they are obviously soiled, although fresh pillowcases are a nice touch. Weather permitting, blankets and especially down comforters and pillows should be aired outdoors daily.

Activity: Prepare a "guest kit" to keep on hand. Include as many of the items listed above as you can, and store them in a box for use when guests visit. (If you are storing aspirin or other medications, be sure to check the expiration dates when you bring them out again.)

Guests should be treated with utmost deference and attended with the same care that you would show the Owner. It is acceptable to ask directly for guidance in serving them, particularly if your Owner is not able to provide details about their preferences. Visiting slaves should be treated like any other guest unless you are specifically told otherwise. If asked to participate in any D/S interactions with someone else's slave, it is perfectly appropriate to ask for verification that the slave has consented to your involvement.

Organizing Dinners and Parties

Although many people enjoy entertaining, few thrive on pre-party stress. Aside from choosing the guests and perhaps the menu, many dominants would gladly turn over the responsibility for planning an event to a competent slave.

When the Owner announces a party, the first thing you should do is check the household calendar to be sure there are no conflicts. Then try to get as much information as possible about the type of event the Owner envisions, the guests, and the budget. Is it an after-theater supper party or a Sunday brunch? A picnic on the beach for two or a black tie affair for two hundred? Note down all the details.

Next, make a list of the different elements of the party: food, drinks, decorations (such as flowers), entertainment (music, dancing). List your sources for each: Food: have groceries delivered, prepare here; Decorations: call florist... If you will be using outside help, such as caterers or a band, call several and compare prices and availability. Remember that the house will need to be cleaned thoroughly, so consider hiring a service a day or two before the party if no other servants are available.

List the tasks you need to accomplish, and create a schedule for yourself. When estimating the amount of time you expect the work to take, add 15% to cover any mishaps. The general rule is to do as much of the preparation as possible before the day of the party. This might include making hors d'oeuvres, selecting recorded music, polishing silver, picking up dry cleaning, cleaning the house, grooming any pets (outside, or before you do the final vacuuming), and arranging cut flowers.

Here is a sample schedule for a moderate-sized dinner party.

Three to four weeks in advance: Draw up guest list and issue invitations. Engage any outside help, such as caterers, musicians, servers, and the like.

Two weeks in advance: Decide on any decorations, including flowers, and make sure you have sufficient kitchen equipment, dishes, linens, and serving utensils. Rent or purchase additional items as needed.

One week in advance: Reconfirm appointments with rental services. Create a food and drink shopping list (remember ice!). Buy decorations as needed. Order flowers. Make sure any special clothing to be worn for the party is cleaned and in good repair.

Three days in advance: Shop for food and prepare any dishes that can be refrigerated or frozen.

Two days in advance: Continue food preparation. Clean house. Arrange tables and move any furniture as needed. Begin any complicated decorating.

One day in advance: Clear out closets or set up racks for coats. Finish decorating. Arrange serving trays, dishes, and utensils. Finish any prep cooking. Fill condiment containers (salt and pepper shakers, sugar bowls). Arrange flowers or have prepared arrangements delivered.

The day of the event: Finish any cooking (or preparations for barbecues) and light cleaning (dusting and straightening up). Stock bathrooms with extra supplies. Set the table. (Information on various place settings can be gleaned for any comprehensive etiquette guide and many general cookbooks.) Chill wines, beers, and mixers as needed. Set up bar, including crispy snacks. Leave time to shower and dress and to assist the Owner with his or her toilette.

Notes on Table Service

During a party, the butler is often in charge of greeting guests and taking their coats, serving drinks, announcing dinner, and serving dinner as well as coffee and drinks afterwards.

When serving individual plates, serve from the guest's left and remove from the right. Beverages are both served and removed from the right. If serving from a cart ("French service"), serve from the right; from a platter ("Russian service"), place plates from the right and holding the platter with your left hand, serve from the left. Silverware should always be carried on a plate, tray, or napkin, plates handled by their edges, and glasses held by the base or stem. Large, light trays should be carried on the left hand above shoulder level; heavier trays may be balanced on the left shoulder. Small trays should be carried in front of you at waist level. Do not remove plates for a given course until everyone has finished. Crumbs can be brushed away with a folded napkin. If smoking is permitted at table, change ashtrays every half-hour or so, or before the next course.

Wine glasses are placed to the right of the water glass, and used glasses should be removed before the next wine is served. Be careful never to touch the rim of a glass when serving. When opening wine, be sure to wipe any mold from the top of the cork. Wipe the lip of the bottle after the cork has been removed and before pouring. Mixed drinks should be served on a tray. If cocktails are regularly served in the household, you should learn to make the Owner's favorites as well as a few classics and whatever the current popular drinks may be. Keep a bartender's manual on hand, too.

As the party ends, you will see the guests safely to the door. You should take note of anyone who seems to have drunk too much and inform the host or hostess immediately (but discreetly, of course). It is the host's responsibility to see that the guest is transported safely home.

Remember to note down details – both successes and failures – in your Butler's Book right after the party.

Activity: The only way to learn about entertaining is to do it. Plan a small dinner party for two to four friends. Include all the basic elements: food, drink, entertainment, and decorations. Write about your experience in your slave journal.

Suggested Reading (see the bibliography for complete references): Letitia Baldrige's Complete Guide to the New Manners for the '90s *[especially good for particulars of table setting and service]; Alexis Bespaloff's* Complete Guide to Wine *(rev. and exp. ed.);* The Pocket Idiot's Guide to Choosing Wine *by Philip Seldon;* Windows on the World Complete Wine Course *by Kevin Zraly;* Mr. Boston Official Bartender's and Party Guide *(64th ed.);* The Complete Cigar Book *by Philip Seldon;* The Complete Book of Entertaining *by Elizabeth Post and Anthony Staffieri;* Bride's Lifetime Guide to Good Food and Entertaining; Entertaining *by Martha Stewart;* Food and Beverage Service Manual *by Matt A. Casado;* Cocktail Parties for Dummies *by Jaymz Bee & Jan Gregor;* The Joys of Entertaining *by Beverley Reese Church & Bethany Ewald Bultman.*

Resources: There are several schools for professional butlers in England and on the continent. The courses run from four to six weeks and cover the details of decorum in depth. The fees start at around $5000, not including room and board. Please note that these schools are for would-be professional servants, not erotic slaves; be discreet in your inquiries.

> *Ivor Spencer School for Butlers*
> *12 Little Bornes*
> *Dulwich, London SE21 8SE*
> *ENGLAND*
> *+44-0181-670-5585*
> *FAX: +44-0181-670-0055*
> *info@IvorSpencer.com*

> *International Thomas School of British Butlers and Household Personnel*
> *36 Rectory Orchard*
> *Lavendon, Olney*
> *Buckinghamshire MK46 4HB*
> *ENGLAND*
> *+44-1234-240544*
> *FAX: +44-1234-240566*

> *International Finishing School for Butlers and Personal Assistants*
> *(opening January 1999)*

Gasthuisstraat 24
4001 BE Tiel
THE NETHERLANDS
+33-344-673937
FAX: +33-344-673938

Information on the International Butlers Association, a professional group, is available at http://www.butlersguild.com.

See also the listing for Starkey International in the lesson on Housekeepers.

ESCORTS

Lesson 40. The Escort

The primary quality for a good escort is social flexibility. In other words, you should be able to make yourself – and other people – comfortable in a variety of social situations, from ball games to ballrooms. If you think of yourself as a "people person," identify as an extrovert, and find that others like and trust you almost immediately, you may have the makings of an escort.

Exercise: To help yourself get a better idea of this role and your interest in it, complete these sentences.

I feel most comfortable around people who...

If asked to identify my social class, I'd say...

When I'm around people speaking a language I don't understand, I...

If a stranger strikes up a conversation with me, I...

My favorite hobbies are...

When I go out on the town, I like to...

People often say I'm...

The most exciting job I've ever had was...

When I meet someone new, I make a point of...

If there's one thing I hate talking about, it's...

If I had to describe my friends, I'd say they're...

When someone asks me a personal question, I feel...

I'd most like to travel to...

The sports I enjoy are...

My favorite cultural activities include...

When people are discussing politics, I...

I think business networking at social functions is...

I feel very uncomfortable when...

Large crowds of strangers make me feel...

I'd estimate I talk to about ... people each day.

When I'm alone, I feel...

When I'm embarrassed, I...

When I'm around a lot of rich people, I feel...

When I'm around a lot of poor people, I feel...

Foreigners visiting this country should...

Gambling is...

When someone brings up the subject of religion, I...

I understand the word "class" to mean...

Read over your answers, and see if you can draw any conclusions about escorting. Write about any insights in your slave journal.

Suggested Reading: How to Start a Conversation and Make Friends by Don Gabor will help you with the basics of conversational politesse. People Skills by Robert Bolton may also be of help. You might enjoy some English novels that focus on the delicate art of sociability: sample Jane Austen, Anthony Trollope, and Angela Thirkell.

Lesson 41. Public Service I: Non-Scene Company

As an escort, you will find that much of your service takes place among persons who are unacquainted with D/S and who might, indeed, be shocked and appalled by the very notion. You must sometimes walk a fine line between fulfilling your obligations and desires as a slave and respecting public norms. Escorts often appear to have greater freedom than some other slaves: they must be allowed to speak freely, to move without encumbrance in crowds, and to act like almost any other person in a given situation in order not to arouse undue suspicion. You may, for example, be asked questions that require you to think quickly and speak discreetly while appearing to be frank: "How do you know [the dominant]?" is a thinly veiled way of asking you to clarify your relationship. Unless you are primarily a personal servant or butler commandeered for an outing, you will not be able to hide behind "duty" to avoid dealing with others in public. And yet you must always maintain awareness of your status and make yourself available to the dominant for use. It is my hope that some of the thoughts in this lesson will help you to navigate more gracefully through society while safeguarding your knowledge of yourself as a slave.

Safety Warning: One reproach commonly hurled at "dangerous" dominants is that they have "gone too far" in public play. What is "too far"? Clearly we are here in the realm of personal opinion. For some, wearing a collar in public would seem risky, while others routinely wear full leather on the street. Miss Abernathy offers the following guidelines regarding limits on public play: A scene has gone too far if it endangers any participant's ongoing ability to care for him- or herself, including that person's physical, mental, psychological, or spiritual well-being, or their capacity to earn a living. For many individuals, that would imply that any public behavior that might result in a slave's losing a job or job status would be unacceptable. Know your limits: what is "too far" for you?

Class and Social Interaction

Although it is sometimes used colloquially as a value judgment ("He has no class" or "She's a classy lady"), the term "class" more properly refers to a complex set of beliefs, feelings, and assumptions that influence how we function socially. Seen from this sociological perspective, "upper class" and "lower class" are descriptors, and carry no value in and of themselves.

Of course, as colloquial usage indicates, class distinctions *do* matter to most people, whether they are aware of them or not – or even, as is sometimes the case, they strive to ignore them.

Why is an understanding of social class important to a slave escort? As an escort, you will be functioning as a companion to a dominant in public settings. Generally you will need to appear as his or her social equal and so you should strive to match your public presentation (dress style, tone of speech, etc.) to the dominant's. If you are both from the same background, this probably won't be difficult; in fact, you may find that part of what drew you to each other was the similarity in your outlooks and assumptions.

If you're from different backgrounds, however, you may find that your views on everything from table manners to leisure reading differ. Further, your own views may differ from those of the company with which you're expected to socialize. If your goal is to serve the dominant by helping him or her present a desired image – and this is the main function of an escort – then it's vital that you know what image you are to present and how to do it.

A simple example, taken from a British study on class and behavior, may illustrate this challenge.* Researchers determined that members of the middle and lower classes are usually taught to apologize by saying "Excuse me" or "Pardon" after they belch. By doing so, they acknowledge that they have engaged in a socially awkward behavior, and respond with an apology. To neglect this apology would be considered insufferably rude. The researchers found that members of the upper class did not excuse themselves after belching. Why? Their social training had taught them that the polite thing to do was simply to ignore socially awkward behavior. By saying "Excuse me," they felt, they were only drawing attention to their mistake, making the whole situation even more awkward. This example shows that even something as insignificant "'Scuse me" mumbled over breakfast can create social tension.

Does this mean that only people from upper class backgrounds can be escorts? Certainly not. The point is that escorts must become aware of social class and learn to respond, not according to the dictates of their upbringing, but as the immediate situation requires.

---

* _Noblesse Oblige_, ed. Nancy Mitford

How can you know what the situation requires? Here Miss Abernathy must defer to the educator's cliché: practice makes perfect. Read all you can (starting with the books I suggest here and in the introduction to the lessons for house servants), hone your observation skills, and be prepared to make mistakes now and then. All the better sort of people do, you know.

Activity: Go to an area of your town or city that you don't usually visit and where you think you'll find people of a different social class. Find a restaurant or café (or diner or coffee shop) and spend an hour or two simply observing the people around you. How do they dress? How do they speak? How do they interact with the servers? Do you feel comfortable there? If so (or even if not), try to pinpoint why. Write about your experience in your slave journal. (Other good locations for people-watching are bus stations, supermarkets in areas you don't frequent, and parks.)

Suggested Reading: Despite its curmudgeonly tone, <u>Class: A Guide through the American Status System</u> by Paul Fussell is still one of the best introductions to American manners. (Caveat lector: Fussell shows an unabashed bias toward the upper classes, often at the expense of the "proles." Unlike him, your job is to learn, not judge, so if you find his humor striking too close to home, you can take solace in the fact that, as an escort, you are all the more prepared for any circumstance.) Literature provides many insights into class: <u>The Great Gatsby</u> by F. Scott Fitzgerald is only the most famous of the American novels that shows the foibles of the rich.

Suggested Viewing: <u>My Fair Lady</u>, the classic musical of class, proves once again that, while social norms run deep, love conquers all.

Conversation

Ideally, escorts should be able to talk to anyone about anything. Indeed, some people seem to be born witty conversationalists. The rest of us must depend on a broad, general education to help us along. Again, you don't need to have graduated cum laude from an Ivy league school to be an escort. In most circles, polite conversation ("small talk") revolves around the people present (or, on occasion, absent) and a relatively narrow range of current events or scandals. You can keep up on these events quite easily.

• Read a good newspaper daily (the **New York Times** is a safe choice).

• Watch a national news broadcast on television or listen to one of the news analyses on National Public Radio.

• Read one or more weekly or monthly newsmagazines (**Time, Newsweek**), plus at least one "cultural" periodical (**The New York Review of Books, The New Yorker**).

• When abroad, read the Herald-Tribune, an international English-language paper available worldwide.

• Make a point of reading – or barring that, skimming – the bestsellers, both fiction and non-fiction.

• Learn about the local sports teams, their major players, and their current standing.

In addition to the newspapers and magazines mentioned above, you will want to familiarize yourself with areas of special interest to your Owner and the people with whom you're most often called upon to converse. (Narcissistic creatures that we are, most people will choose to spend their time with those rather like themselves. If you know what interests your Owner, you're halfway to knowing what interests his or her friends.) The list below will help you locate some of the standard reference volumes for topics as diverse as opera, bridge, art, and basketball. In the meantime, the following two titles will help you fill in any immediate gaps: An Incomplete Education by Judy Jones and William Wilson and Everything You Pretend to Know and Are Afraid Someone Will Ask by Lynette Padua.

When conversing, particularly in a public setting, it is important to remember these few guidelines:

• Try not to dominate the conversation or monopolize any one individual. Ask questions that encourage others to speak.

• Unless the setting clearly implies and encourages them, avoid emotionally charged topics like religion or politics.

- In some circles, displaying your intellectual prowess, education level, or technical knowledge will brand you a snob or a bore, hardly appropriate appellations for a slave. Try to assess the content, level, and style of the conversation before you jump in.

Suggested Reading: <u>Benét's Reader's Encyclopedia</u> (4th ed.) ed. Bruce Murphy; <u>The New Complete Hoyle</u> Revised by Albert H. Morehead, Richard L. Frey & Geoffrey Mott-Smith [rules for games]; <u>Learn Bridge in a Weekend</u> by Jonathan David; <u>Play Winning Chess</u> by Yasser Seirawan; <u>The Sports Rules Book</u> by Human Kinetics with Thomas Hanlon; <u>The Complete Idiot's Guide to... and ...for Dummies</u> sports series (covers football, golf, baseball, etc.); <u>Understanding Art</u> by Gene Mittler and Rosalind Ragans; <u>The Story of Art</u> (16th ed.) by E. H. Gombrich; <u>Key Art Terms for Beginners</u> by Philip Yenawine; <u>Film as Art</u> by Rudolph Arnheim; <u>The Guide to Classic Recorded Jazz</u> by Tom Piazza; <u>The New Kobbé's Opera Book</u> ed. The Earl of Harewood and Antony Peattie; <u>Opera 101</u> by Fred Plotkin; <u>Opera: The Rough Guide</u> by Matthew Boyden; <u>The NPR Classical Music Companion</u> by Miles Hoffman.

Lesson 42. Public Service II: Scene Company

For many slaves, serving at a public BDSM function is a rare treat and a great honor. For others, "scene" events may be the only safe semi-public environment in which to display their roles and relationship and are therefore the site of most or all of their public play. In either case, the code of behavior in the scene is markedly different from that of non-scene events.

Even if you have never attended a BDSM community gathering, you will be able to imagine some of the more obvious differences. First and foremost, it is assumed that virtually everyone present is part of the scene. (Those who are not, sometimes dubbed "tourists," are usually painfully obvious.) You do not need to hide your relationships or lifestyle; in fact, you are encouraged to flaunt them. Depending on the type of event, you may see others engaged in a wide range of sexual and non-sexual activities, many of which would be unthinkable in other public surroundings.

Activity: Attend a public BDSM gathering. It may be a social group meeting, an educational program, a bar event such as a contest, or a play party. Observe the dynamics of the group. Who seems to command respect? How are unattached submissives treated (and can you readily identify them)? How would you describe the "unspoken rules" that govern behavior? How is deference shown? If there is a dress code for the event, what is it? If there is no formal dress code, how great is the range of styles you see? Can you identify any slaves with their Owners? How do they act? What visible services, if any, do they perform? Describe your experiences in your slave journal.

Your observations in this exercise will depend heavily on the type of event you attend (party, group meeting, contest), the group itself (single-gender or mixed), and the city or region. If possible, try to attend a variety of events over a period of time and see if your observations change.

If the most difficult part of serving in non-scene company is maintaining a sense of submission and decorum, the greatest challenge for slaves when serving in scene company is keeping their focus. Play parties, in particular, are like three-ring circuses, with distracting sights and sounds at every turn. The fact of being on display can be both tantalizing and terrifying for slaves. If you are accustomed to serving one person in the safe confines of your house, the sudden flood of attention can be dizzying.

Activity: Look back over your work for this course. What skills have you already learned that can help you maintain your composure and focus at a BDSM event? Meditation, affirmations... Practice these techniques daily.

Suggested Reading: Jay Wiseman's SM 101 *contains a list of some of the BDSM social and educational groups around the US as well as a very helpful chapter on "SM Organizations" which will ease your entree into the scene and help you locate like-minded others.*

Lesson 43. Travel

Traveling with a dominant can be among the most pleasurable activities for a slave, but it brings with it some of the greatest practical challenges. We have all heard the catalogue of nightmares that travelers face: canceled flights, lost luggage, jet lag, forgotten medications, sheer exhaustion. With careful planning and a little luck, however, most of these troubles can be avoided.

Exercise: List five ways in which your experiences traveling as a slave might differ from your experiences traveling alone. Now, list five ways in which serving while traveling might differ from serving at home. What new situations might you encounter? What new or unusual responsibilities or tasks might you be called upon to perform? How could you best prepare for those possibilities?

If organizing a journey has been left to you and you are not familiar with your destination, by all means avail yourself of the expertise of a travel agent. Give the agent as much information as possible (including any budgeting restrictions) and s/he will save you untold hours listening to hold music as you phone hotels and airlines.

When it comes to packing bags, Miss Abernathy is a firm believer in the value of lists. Start with the Clothing Inventory that you compiled during Personal Servant training. Keeping in mind the length of the trip and the accessibility of laundry services, select garments that 1) pack well (no linen!); 2) suit the climate of your destination; 3) are appropriate for the activities the dominant will be undertaking (business, sight-seeing, sports); 4) all coordinate with each other. (See the suggested reading for travel wardrobe ideas and a truly brilliant packing system.) Make a list of the items as you pack them and put one copy in the suitcase and carry a second copy with you. (These lists can come in handy if your luggage is lost or if you send clothing out to be cleaned.)

Toiletries should be packed in airtight bags; medications should be carried on board. Sex toys and SM gear should be checked, however, as airport security agents seem to take great delight in questioning travelers about them. (Handcuffs cannot be taken in carry-on luggage at all, even when they are obviously ornamental.)

Activity: Practice packing an overnight bag. Ideally, you should be able to pack all the necessities for a weekend trip in under 15 minutes. (Set a timer.) What would you have to do to pack in 5 minutes?

Suggested Reading: The Packing Book *by Judith Gilford.*

Slaves who travel regularly would do well to study foreign languages to the best of their abilities. After English, French is the most commonly understood international language, but you should give preference to the languages spoken in the destinations you most often visit.

Resources: Most major cities have private language schools, and most community colleges offer beginning conversation courses in a variety of languages. If you are looking for a private tutor, call the appropriate foreign language department at your local college or university. Graduate students can have considerable teaching experience and are often grateful for the extra income.

V. Advanced Studies

Congratulations on completing the Area Studies section of the course. By now you will have attained a deeper knowledge of your own skills and talents and will have chosen one or more areas of specialization.

At this point, you may be considering a greater commitment to this life. Many slaves fantasize about a full-time, "live-in" relationship that will allow them to live as a slave without interruption. It is possible to arrange a "24/7" (i.e., 24 hours a day, 7 days a week) contract, but it should not be entered into lightly. The lessons that follow will help you examine some of the issues that arise as you contemplate this step. We will also cover some related subjects, such as permanent marks, serving multiple owners, and training other slaves. Finally, in preparation for your final project, we will explore in more detail how a slave can live ethically in submission to another person.

Again, congratulations on your work to this point, and best of luck as you approach the end of the course.

Lesson 44. Live-In Arrangements I: Pragmatic Considerations

If you are considering a live-in arrangement, there are any number of issues you must review before signing or even negotiating a contract with a dominant. Please review Manual, pp. 56-57, for a brief overview of the different models for live-ins, then take the following diagnostic quiz.

Exercise: Choose the answer that best reflects your ideas.

1. As a live-in, I'd live at...
a. our house.

b. his/her house.

c. an in-law apartment at his/her house.

2. I'd earn my living...

a. at the same job I had before.

b. Those days are over. Master provides for me now.

c. doing part-time work for Master's business.

3. We/I have...

a. A joint checking account.

b. A custodial account in Mistress's name.

c. My own checking and savings accounts.

4. After signing a contract, I could move in with Master...

a. Move in? I already live here!

b. any time. As long as he pays the movers, of course.

c. once I settled my affairs and put my things in storage.

5. The best thing about a live-in contract is...

a. formalizing our D/S relationship.

b. giving up complete control of my affairs.

c. being able to work at home and still be a slave.

6. Mistress is...

a. employed outside the home, as am I.

b. easily able to provide for both of us.

c. self-employed.

7. My only dependents are...

a. my grown children.

b. my goldfish.

c. my dog.

8. What I enjoy most about submission is...

a. how well Master and I complement each other.

b. feeling completely in Master's hands.

c. being useful and competent.

9. When I file my taxes, I use...
a. the 1040A form.
b. the 1040EZ form.
c. the 1040 form with the SE and C schedules.

10. The car is registered...
a. in both our names.
b. in Mistress's name.
c. in my name.

11. The answering machine says...
a. "the Jones residence"
b. "Mr. Jones' residence"
c. "Press one for Mr. Jones. Press two for Miss Smith..."

12. If I weren't a slave, I'd be...
a. gainfully employed. Gotta pay the rent!
b. socking away my income...know a good broker?
c. building up my own business.

13. The neighbors think...
a. we're swinger types.
b. I'm a gold digger.
c. I'm his secretary.

14. Our arrangement makes me feel...
a. loved.
b. desired.
c. needed.

15. The hardest part of our arrangement is...
a. keeping our roles going day-to-day.
b. worrying about how I'd manage if Mistress threw me out.
c. remembering my place.

If you chose mostly (a) answers, you would do well with the partnership model. You are probably already in a committed relationship with a dominant, or are in the process of exploring dominance and submission with your long-term partner. While you're serious about submission, you recognize that financial necessity and the other commitments you may have to family prevent you from giving up your job. You prefer that your D/S relationship be private (perhaps you share your status with some close friends who may also be "in the scene"). You don't care if you retain some control over your day-to-day affairs, since your role as a slave is more about how you feel about your partner and how the two of you work together. You may want to experiment with other styles of submission. For example, the two of you can rent a hotel room or cabin for a Master/Mistress and slave weekend.

If you chose mostly (b) answers, you are most attracted to the dependent model. While this model is the one most often depicted in BDSM fiction, it is relatively rare in real life. Most households require two incomes to function, but if either you or the dominant has sufficient assets, this model may work for you. There are two major caveats: first, slavehood is not a substitute for employment. If you have trouble holding down a job, you will find it difficult to be a slave, as slavehood involves even more personal responsibility than most paid jobs. Second, get it in writing. If you are turning over assets to a dominant, Miss Abernathy strongly recommends that you contact a lawyer to draw up a pre-nuptial (or domestic partnership) agreement that spells out in detail what you are bringing to the household and what is due you should it dissolve. Both parties should have current wills as well. You may also want to agree upon a way of safeguarding your prospects should you need to return to outside employment. The dominant may be willing to refer to you as a "personal assistant" for job search purposes.

If you chose mostly (c) answers, you are best suited for the employee model. You come to the relationship with considerable business skills, and you want to retain some amount of autonomy and control over your work. The dominant may work from home and engage you part-time as an assistant or consultant. This model can be challenging to your submission, as it is sometimes hard to switch from super-efficient businessperson to "lowly" slave after hours. Also, by linking your work life to your personal life, you run the risk of losing both if one goes sour.

Still, if you enjoy feeling needed and are secure in your abilities, this model may be workable for you.

Lesson 45. Live-In Arrangements II: Financial Considerations

The diagnostic test in the last lesson should have given you some idea of the financial realities that live-in slaves face. Depending on the type of arrangement you enter into – partnership, dependent, or employee – you may have to make some important changes in your financial situation.

Activity: (Note: Consider hiring a financial professional to help you with this exercise.) Take stock of your financial situation. What is your net worth? Are you in debt? Are you in default on any loans or consumer debts (credit cards)? If you were to quit work today, how long would you be able to cover your (current) expenses? What is the minimum amount of money you think you could live on? Do you expect to inherit any money? Do you own valuables like jewelry, antiques, art...?

Suggested Reading: Get a Financial Life by Beth Kobliner is a straightforward introduction to personal finance. Though written with younger people in mind, it will be useful to all.

Activity: Make a list of all your accounts, investments, and valuable property. Have this document notarized and put it in a safe deposit box.

Activity: Design a budget based on your desired live-in status. Don't forget necessities like health insurance as well as any uniforms, toiletries, and other needs. How could you simplify your lifestyle and cut down expenses?

Suggested Reading: Elaine St. James has authored several little volumes on simple living which provide hundreds of money-saving tips.

Talking about money isn't very romantic, but it is one of the most often overlooked aspects of slave training and in relationships of all kinds. If money becomes a source of conflict in your negotiations, please take the time to discuss not just the dollars-and-cents particulars, but your feelings about money itself. How was money handled in your family of origin? How important is it to you to have money in your pocket? Do you feel uncomfortable if you don't have next month's rent in the bank by the 15th? What does money symbolize to you: security? freedom? status? By talking frankly about your feelings, you will be better able to negotiate a mutually agreeable way to handle finances in your relationship.

Lesson 46. Live-In Arrangements III: Emotional Considerations

In the last two lessons, we have already begun to look at some of the emotional ramifications of live-in arrangements. Before proceeding with this lesson, please review the following lessons: "Assessing Strengths and Weaknesses," "Assessing Risk," and "What Kind of Slave Am I?" You may want to do the exercises in these lessons again, now that you have a broader knowledge of the responsibilities of a slave.

While the exercises here are brief, they are meant to be completed slowly. Take your time, and write as much as you need to. Then share your responses with your trainer or dominant, as appropriate.

Exercise: Name the emotions that you feel when you think about the prospect of a live-in arrangement.

Exercise: In your slave journal, write a list of your fears regarding a live-in relationships. Do not censor yourself. All your "silly" fears are legitimate and valid. Be prepared to share these fears with your prospective Owner in a candid fashion and to think of ways to allay them.

Exercise: Using the 1-10 exercise in "Assessing Risk," write at least a paragraph on the subject "Being 'Out' as a Slave." How does other people's awareness of your status affect you, your Owner, and others in your life? Does a live-in arrangement change that awareness? How do you feel about the possibility of criticism from family, friends, or authority figures? If you are uncomfortable with being "out," what measures would you need to take to safeguard your privacy? What limits might this place on your relationships?

Lesson 47. Permanent Marks: Piercing

In the Manual (pp. 28-30) I discussed a variety of ways that dominants may choose to physically mark their slaves as a sign of ownership, commitment, and devotion. Here we will focus on the method most commonly associated with slavehood: piercing.

Exercise: Complete the following sentences:

The kind of piercing I like the most is...

I'm afraid of being pierced because...

People who have piercings...

If s/he saw my piercing, my physician would...

If s/he saw my piercing, my best friend would...

If they knew I was pierced, my family members would...

If I were pierced, I would be embarrassed to...

Erotically, piercing would...

Piercing would affect my submission by...

Note: If you are considering another form of permanent marking, like a tattoo, branding, or scarification (cutting), use this exercise by substituting the name of your preferred method of marking.

Exercise: In your slave journal, write about the associations that permanent body piercings have to you. Do you have any body piercings? Why did you choose them? Did they mark a particular event in your life? How do you feel about them now? Have you ever let a piercing heal over? Why? If you have no piercings, do you know anyone who does? Have you seen pictures of piercings? How did they make you feel?

Activity: Visit a professional piercer. (Most major North American cities have at least one.) Many will have printed information for you to take home, and they'll be happy to talk with you about their techniques and training. (Reputable body piercers will not use piercing guns except, perhaps, for earlobes; will have an autoclave; and will not recommend sterling silver jewelry for body piercings.) If there is no piercer in your area, or if you feel uncomfortable with your local piercer, it is much better to wait until you can visit San Francisco, New York, Los Angeles, Amsterdam, London, or Paris, all of which have many well-trained, responsible piercers.

Suggested Reading: Story of O by Pauline Réage. How does O interpret her rings? What do they mean to her?

Resources: Gauntlet, one of the oldest and largest piercing studios in the world, produces a series of videos on piercing as well as a magazine and jewelry. While I do not suggest that you try permanent piercing at home, you may find it reassuring to view a video that explains the specific technique for the piercing you want. Gauntlet, San Francisco, can be reached at (415) 431-3133. See also Manual, pp. 83-84 for a list of body modification artists. Slaves with Internet access should avail themselves of the Frequently Asked Questions file posted periodically to the rec.arts.bodyart newsgroup.

Lesson 48. Serving Multiple Owners

While most of this book has been written with the assumption that you will be serving one other individual, it is now time to look at another possibility: serving multiple owners. Most often, this involves serving a couple, but it may also include a ménage of three or more.

If you are considering the possibility of serving a couple or a ménage, you face some special challenges. First, you may be worked harder, since tasks tend to increase exponentially with the number of people you serve. Second, you may find yourself struggling with favoritism (your own and the Owners'). Third, you may be caught in a conflict of wills, as when one Owner wants a task performed a certain way and the other wants it done differently or not at all. Finally, your status as slave may be dependent on the stability of your Owners' relationship. If their arrangement ends, how will it affect you?

Serving multiple owners does have some distinct advantages as well. You may get more individual attention and care, including more sex, if that is part of your arrangement. You will have a chance to develop more flexibility and better communication skills. You may experience a greater variety of types of service, as the different owners express different needs. You will benefit by the different training styles and experiences that the owners may exhibit. You will also have the privilege of witnessing an intimate relationship as the partners weather the seasons and changes that life brings.

Exercise: Write a short essay on the theme of "Polyfidelity." (Some people prefer this term to "non-monogamy" as a way to refer to multiple committed relationships. For more information, see the suggested reading list.) What does the word suggest to you? What qualities would you need to bring to such a relationship? What challenges would it present to you personally?

Exercise: List five special things that you might need to negotiate for in a contract between you and a couple.

Activity: If possible, talk with someone involved in a long-term polyamorous relationship. (If you don't know anyone in this situation, please explore the suggested reading carefully and, if you have Internet access, read the newsgroup alt.polyamory for a while.) What difficulties have they encountered? How do they deal with conflict? What advantages do they see in their relationship? What advice do they have for you?

Suggested Reading: The Ethical Slut by Dossie Easton and Catherine A. Liszt is a sensible, BDSM-friendly guide to multiple relationships of all sorts. Other titles dealing with polyamory (multiple love relationships) and polyfidelity are Breaking the Barriers to Desire: Polyamory, Polyfidelity, and Non-monogamy ed. Kevin Lano and Claire Parry, Loving More: The Polyfidelity Primer, by Ryam Nearing, and Polyamory: The New Love

Without Limits by Deborah Anapol. *(All the titles listed here received high ratings for "pro-poly" perspective from the alt.polyamory newsgroup, as reported in the group's Frequently Asked Questions Cultural Supplement.)*

Lesson 49. Training Others

One of the greatest displays of confidence that a dominant can make is to allow an experienced slave to train a new submissive. The dominant may not have time to attend to new slaves-in-training or may feel that an experienced servant can better prepare them for their roles. Sometimes, in the course of training, it becomes apparent that a slave, while happily and willingly submissive to the Owner, may also have a dominant side that requires expression. Further, some service roles described above, like housekeepers and butlers, are essentially household managers, and as such require the ability to train underlings. In all of these cases, the opportunity to train another person may fill a slave with pride and expectant joy.

If you are asked to train a slave yourself, you must take time and care to determine if you are equal to the task. You should also carefully examine your feelings: are you likely to feel jealous of the newcomer? If you are experiencing any frustrations in your own submission, you may find yourself taking them out on your trainee, or subtly undermining your own training efforts. It may help you to know that many experienced dominants were once, themselves, slaves. If this is the case with your Owner, you may be able to speak frankly with him or her and derive some measure of reassurance from his or her experiences.

Exercise: Write down any fears that you have about training a new slave. No fear is "too silly"; all are valid. You may want to use your meditation time to explore some of these fears.

Activity: Read back over your slave journal from start to finish. What obstacles, internal or external, did you face when you began your training? How did you overcome them? Which do you still consider troubling?

Remember that if you have worked your way steadily through this study course, you now have a great wealth of experience to draw on. You know yourself better than many people do, and you are better able to articulate your ideas and feelings. Perhaps you have even felt the stirrings of a spiritual dimension to your submission. These are gifts; share them freely.

Suggested Reading: Review the basic BDSM texts listed in the introduction to the Sex Slave section. You may also want to read some of the D/S classics mentioned in Manual, pp. 71-75.

Lesson 50. Ethical Slavehood

When asked to explain their desires, many submissives will say that they enjoy letting go of responsibility for their actions, if only for a time. It is true that the burdens of life can weigh heavily on our shoulders, and it is refreshing to feel the lightness and freedom of childhood when we needed only do as we were told for the world to seem a bright and safe place.

However, by now I hope you have come to see slavehood as more than escapism. As a slave, you do not give up your will. You learn to attune it to another person's, until the two are as one. This is the real source of that "second sense" that some experienced slaves have: they know their Owners so well that they experience the Owners' needs and desires as their own. In a sense, then, rather than giving up responsibility, a slave becomes doubly accountable.

Undoubtedly you will encounter minor circumstances in which you are called upon to act against your better judgment. After all, intimate relationships often require us to set aside our own desires in favor of our partner's preferences, at least once in a while. Sometimes these requests are illogical, but their importance rests in the realm of emotions, and so we act. This is all the more true in dominant/submissive relationships.

And yet we are still people, frail in our humanity. Dominants are not all-powerful; slaves are not omniscient. Further, even in the most well-planned lives, reality rudely intrudes. How do you, as a slave, maintain a firm ethical foundation when your will and that of the Owner are at odds?

In the following exercise, I ask you to spend some time thinking carefully about how you would respond to some difficult situations. Write about your thoughts and doubts in your slave journal. There are no right answers here; each of these situations involves moral ambiguity, with plenty of shades of gray. Please share your answers with your trainer and be prepared to discuss them frankly.

Exercise: How would you respond to these situations? What might you do to prevent them? Can you imagine circumstances that might make other choices understandable and acceptable, for yourself or others?

1. Your contract stipulates safer sex. One night, your Owner orders you to "forget the condom." What do you do?

2. Your Owner asks you to purchase illegal drugs for his/her use. What do you do?

3. You are a personal secretary, and you become aware that your Owner is committing tax fraud. What do you do?

4. Your Owner is a non-custodial parent. Just a few minutes before the child is due to arrive for a weekend visit, the Owner orders you to strip for sex. What do you do?

5. Your contract allows for you to be lent out to your Owner's dominant friends. Recently your Owner has become close with someone about whom you've heard negative gossip that leads you to believe they may be dangerous. Now your Owner wants to lend you to this person. What do you do?

6. Some close friends of your Owner's visit. After their departure, you discover that some money is missing. What do you do?

7. Your contract stipulates that you and your Owner will have unprotected sex only with each other. You have kept your word, but you discover you have contracted an STD. What do you do?

8. One of the Owner's credit cards is missing. You know you didn't touch it, but the Owner accuses you. What do you do?

9. You become aware that your Owner is developing a bad reputation in your local BDSM community. What do you do?

10. Your Owner beats you non-consensually. You leave the relationship. Soon after, you hear that a novice submissive is seeing your former Owner. What do you do?

Submission has sometimes been referred to as "consensual co-dependency." From the outside, a dominant/submissive relationship may appear emotionally unbalanced, even abusive. With consent as an ethical bottom line, however, BDSM practitioners are able to enjoy power play without undermining any participant's essential human rights. Even as a slave, you do retain those rights, morally and legally.

Suggested Reading: How to Be an Adult: A Handbook on Psychological and Spiritual Integration by David Richo outlines a program for building good boundaries, dealing with difficult emotions, and promoting self-esteem. This is an excellent guide, even for therapy "veterans."

VI. Final Project

My heartfelt congratulations to you! You have completed the Academy's training course and are ready to put together your final project. The final project is a major undertaking, in your special field of interest, that displays your knowledge and achievement in that field.

If you are working with a trainer, he or she will make suggestions for a final project. If you are working alone, you may choose an appropriate project for yourself.

Take your time in choosing and completing the project. (I suggest two to three weeks.) If possible, the project should be at least semi-public, but you may "serve" a willing friend if no dominant is available to you.

Some suggestions for final projects:

- Butlers can arrange a small dinner party for a friend.
- Ladies' maids can give a friend a makeover.
- Escorts can accompany a friend to the opera.
- Housekeepers can spring-clean a friend's house.
- Personal secretaries can offer to organize a self-employed friend's home office.
- Sex slaves can offer a massage (erotic or not) to a friend.

Do not feel limited by these suggestions. By giving of yourself, even in a friendly way, you are honoring your submissive nature and creating good will. What greater gift do we have to offer?

VII. Conclusion

Gentle reader...

As we end our time together, please take some time to review all that you have accomplished since you began this course. I hope that you have come to feel, as I do, that slavehood is a noble and honorable path.

You may find yourself excited about the path ahead of you. If you are still searching for a dominant to serve, take heart in the fact that your dedication to bettering yourself through self-directed training can only make you more attractive to those who know the value of service. If you are already in service, I wish you all the delights and wonders that this path may bring. A slave's training is never really finished, as there is always some new skill, some new specialty that draws you onward.

Until we meet again, I remain, etc.

Christina Abernathy (Miss)

ANNOUNCING
MISS ABERNATHY'S ACADEMY

offering correspondence courses based on the methods outlined in
Training with Miss Abernathy and Miss Abernathy's Concise Slave
Training Manual.
- Individual tutoring with Miss Abernathy
- Personalized training – no form letters
- Discreet mailings – your privacy assured
- Basic Training courses from $375

For information and an application, write to:
Miss Christina Abernathy
Post Office Box 460132
San Francisco, California 94146-0132
U.S.A.

Selected Bibliography

ISBNs appear in brackets after the listing.

Abernathy, Christina. Miss Abernathy's Concise Slave Training Manual. Greenery, 1996. [0963976397]

Adamson, Sara. The Slave. Rhinoceros, 1994. [156333173X]

Albano, John R. Haircutting at Home. Berkley, 1995. [042514688X]

Allen, Christopher and Kimberly Burton Allen. A Butler's Life: Scenes from the Other Side of the Silver Salver. Beil, 1997. [091372095X]

Anand, Margo. The Art of Sexual Ecstasy. Tarcher/Putnam, 1989. [0874775817]

Anderson, Dan and Maggie Berman. Sex Tips for Straight Women from a Gay Man. HarperCollins, 1997. [0060392320]

Arnheim, Rudolph. Film as Art. U. of Califoria Press, 1957. [0520000358]

Aslett, Don. The Cleaning Encyclopedia. Dell, 1993. [0440504813]

Aucoin, Kevyn. Making Faces. Little Brown, 1997. [0316286869]

Bannon, Race. Learning the Ropes: A Basic Guide to Safe and Fun S/M Lovemaking. Daedalus, 1993. [1881943070]

Baugh, L. Sue. How to Write First-Class Letters. NTC, 1994. [0844240990]

Bee, Jaymz and Jan Gregor. Cocktail Parties for Dummies. IDG, 1997. [0764550268]

Berkowitz, Bob. His Secret Life. Simon & Schuster, 1997. [0684811030]

Berthold-Bond. Clean & Green: The Complete Guide to Nontoxic and Environmentally Safe Housekeeping. Ceres, 1990. [0960613838]

——. The Green Kitchen Handbook. Harper Perennial, 1997. [0060951869]

Bespaloff, Alexis. Alexis Bespaloff's Complete Guide to Wine. rev. ed. Signet, 1994. [0451181697]

Blank, Joani, ed. I Am My Lover: Women Pleasure Themselves. Down There Press, 1997 [0940208180]

Blumenthal, Lassor A. The Art of Letter Writing. Perigee, 1977. [0399511741]

Bolton, Robert. People Skills. Touchstone, 1979. [067162248X]

Boostrom, Robert. Developing Creative & Critical Thinking: An Intergrated Approach. NTC, 1992.

Bornstein, Kate. My Gender Workbook. Routledge, 1998. [0415916739]

Boston Women's Health Book Collective. The New Our Bodies, Ourselves. Touchstone, 1992. [0684823527]

Boyden, Matthew. Opera: The Rough Guide. Rough Guides, 1997. [1858281385]

Boyles, Dennis et al. The Modern Man's Guide to Life. Harper Perennial, 1987. [0060961333]

Bride's Lifetime Guide to Good Food & Entertaining. Congdon & Weed, 1984. [0865531137]

Califia, Pat. Sapphistry: the Book of Lesbian Sexuality. 3rd ed. Naiad, 1988. [094148324X]

——. Sensuous Magic. 2nd ed. Masquerade, 1998. [1563336103]

——, ed. The Lesbian S/M Safety Manual. Lace, 1988. [1555833012]

—— and Drew Campbell, eds. Bitch Goddess: the Spiritual Path of the Dominant Woman. Greenery, 1998. [1890159042]

Cameron, Julia and Mark Bryan. The Artist's Way: A Spiritual Path to Higher Creativity. Putnam, 1992. [0874776945]

Campbell, Jeff and the Clean Team. Speed Cleaning. Dell, 1997. [0440503744]

Casado, Matt A. Food and Beverage Service Guide. Wiley, 1994. [0471304646]

Cash, Thomas F. The Body Image Workbook. New Harbinger, 1997. [1572240628]

Child, Julia. The Way to Cook. Knopf, 1996. [0394532643]

Complete Book of Sewing. DK, 1996. [0789404192]

Corey, Kathy and Lynne Blackman. Rituals for the Bath. Warner, 1995. [0446910929]

Curtis, Lucy D. Lucy's List. Warner, 1995. [0446672831]

Davidson, Jeff. The Complete Idiot's Guide to Managing Your Time. Alpha Books, 1995. [0028610393]

Davis, Jonathan. Learn Bridge in a Weekend. Knopf, 1996. [067942752X]

Doner, Kalia and Margaret Doner. The Wellness Center's Spa at Home. Berkley, 1997. [0425157695]

Easton, Dossie and Catherine A. Liszt. The Ethical Slut: A Guide to Infinite Sexual Possibilities. Greenery, 1997. [1890159018]

Eisenberg, Ronni and Kate Kelly. The Overwhelmed Person's Guide to Time Management. Plume, 1997. [0452276829]

Flusser, Alan. Clothes and the Man: the Principles of Fine Men's Dress. Villard, 1994. [0394546237]

Fontanel, Béatrice. Support and Seduction: A History of Corsets and Bras. Abrams, 1997. [0810940868]

Fussell, Paul. Class: A Guide through the American Status System. Touchstone, 1983. [0671792253]

Gabor, Don. How to Start a Conversation and Make Friends. Fireside, 1983. [0671474219]

Gendler, J. Ruth. The Book of Qualities. Harper Perennial, 1988. [0060962526]

Gilford, Judith. The Packing Book: Secrets of the Carry-on Traveler. Ten Speed Press, 1996. [0898158214]

Gombrich, E.H. The Story of Art. 16th ed. Phaidon, 1995. [0714832472]

Greskovic, Robert. Ballet 101. Hyperion, 1998. [0786881550]

Gross, Kim Johnson et al. Woman's Face: Skin Care and Makeup. Knopf, 1997. [0679445781]

——. Work Clothes: Casual Dress for Serious Work. Knopf, 1996. [0679447164]

Hoffman, Miles. The NPR Classical Music Companion. Houghton Mifflin, 1997. [0392707420]

Human Kinetics with Thomas Hanlon, The Sports Rules Book. Human Kinetics, 1998. [0880118075]

Hynes, Angela. The Pleasures of Afternoon Tea. HP Books, 1987. [0895865793]

Ishiguro, Kazuo. The Remains of the Day. Vintage, 1993. [0679731725]

Jackson, Carole and Kalia Lulow. Color for Men. Ballantine, 1984. [0345345460]

Johnson, Carol A. Self-Esteem Comes in All Sizes. Main Street, 1995. [0382475691]

Jones, Judy and William Wilson. An Incomplete Education. Ballantine, 1995. [0345391373]

Kamman, Madeleine. The New Making of a Cook. Morrow, 1997. [0688152546]

Kanarek, Lisa. Organizing Your Home Office for Success. Plume, 1993. [0452268338]

Kent, Cassandra. Household Hints & Tips. DK, 1996. [078940432X]

——. Organizing Hints & Tips. DK, 1997. [078941998X]

Klensch, Elsa. Style. Perigee, 1995. [0399521526]

Kobliner, Beth. Get a Financial Life. Fireside, 1996. [0684812134]

Lehmkuhl, Dorothy and Dolores Cotter Lamping. Organizing for the Creative Person. Crown, 1993. [0517991640]

MacMurray, Jessica M. and Allison Brewster Franzetti. The Book of 101 Opera Librettos. Black Dog & Leventhal, 1997. [1884822797]

Martin, Judith. Miss Manners' Guide to Excruciatingly Correct Behavior. Warner, 1982. [0446386324]

Meyer, Harold E. Lifetime Encyclopedia of Letters. rev. & exp. ed. Prentice Hall, 1992. [0135295467]

Mitchell, Stewart. The Complete Illustrated Guide to Massage. Element, 1997. [1852309903]

Mitford, Nancy, ed. Noblesse Oblige: An Enquiry into the Identifiable Characteristics of the English Aristocracy. Atheneum, 1986. [0689707045]

Mittler, Gene and Rosalind Ragans. Understanding Art. Glencoe, 1992. [0026622866]

Molloy, John T. Molloy's Live for Success. Morrow, 1981. [0688004121]

Morehead, Albert H. et al. The New Complete Hoyle Revised. Doubleday, 1987. [0385249624]

Morin, Jack. Anal Pleasure and Health. Yes Press, 1986. [0940208083]

Mr. Boston Official Bartender's and Party Guide. 64th ed. Warner, 1994. [0446670421]

Murphy, Bruce, ed. Benét's Reader's Encyclopedia. HarperCollins, 1996. [006270110X]

Nagle, Jill, ed. Whores and Other Feminists. Routledge, 1997. [0415918227]

Nierenberg, Gerald I. and Henry H. Calero. How to Read a Person Like a Book. Pocket Books, 1971. [0671735578]

Ordesky, Maxine. The Complete Home Organizer. Grove, 1993. [0802133401]

Padwa, Lynette. Everything You Pretend to Know and Are Afraid Someone Will Ask. Penguin, 1996. [0140513221]

Piazza, Tom. The Guide to Classic Recorded Jazz. U of Iowa Press, 1995. [0877454892]

Plotkin, Fred. Opera 101. Hyperion, 1994. [0786880252]

Popov, Linda Kavelin. Sacred Moments: Daily Meditations on the Virtues. Plume, 1997. [0452278112]

Post, Elizabeth and Anthony Staffieri. The Complete Book of Entertaining. Harper & Row, 1981. [069001970X]

Post, Peggy. Emily Post's Etiquette. 16th ed. HarperCollins: 1997. [0062700782]

Preston, John. Mr. Benson. Badboy, 1992. [1563330415]

Professional Secretary's Handbook. 3rd ed. Houghton Mifflin, 1995. [0395696216]

Quant, Mary. Ultimate Makeup & Beauty. DK, 1996. [0789410567]

Queen, Carol. Exhibitionism for the Shy. Down There Press, 1995. [0940208164]

Réage, Pauline. Story of O. Ballantine, 1989. [0345301110]

Rombauer, Irma S. et al. Joy of Cooking. Scribner, 1997. [0684818701]

Rubenstein, Hal and Jim Mullen. Paisley Goes with Nothing: A Man's Guide to Style. Doubleday, 1995. [0385477120]

Sangster, Rob. Traveler's Tool Kit: How to Travel Absolutely Anywhere. Menasha Ridge Press, 1996. [0897322010]

Seirawan, Yasser. Play Winning Chess. Microsoft, 1995.

Seldon, Philip. The Complete Cigar Book. Ballantine, 1997. [0345422007]

——. The Pocket Idiot's Guide to Choosing Wine. Alpha, 1997. [002862016X]

Simon, Sidney B. In Search of Values. Warner, 1993. [0446394378]

Simpson, Helen. The London Ritz Book of Afternoon Tea. Arbor House, 1986. [0877958238]

Smith, Michael. The Afternoon Tea Book. Collier, 1986. [0020103514]

Spencer, John and Adrian Pruss. The Professional Secretary's Management Skills. Barron's, 1997. [0764100246]

Steiner, Claude and Paul Perry. Achieving Emotional Literacy. Avon, 1997. [0380975912]

Stewart, Martha. Entertaining. Clarkson Potter, 1982. [0517544199]

Sullivan, Lou. Information for the Female to Male Cross Dresser and Transsexual. 3rd ed. Ingersoll Gender Center, 1990.

Taormino, Tristan. The Ultimate Guide to Anal Sex for Women. Cleis, 1998. [1573440280]

Thibault, Kelly J. Leather and Latex Care: How to Keep Your Leather and Latex Looking Great. Daedalus, 1996. [1881943003]

Turner, E.S. What the Butler Saw. St. Martin's, 1962.

Veblen, Thorstein. The Theory of the Leisure Class. Penguin, 1994. [0140187952]

Vera, Veronica. Miss Vera's Finishing School for Boys Who Want to Be Girls. Main Street, 1997. [0385484569]

Warren, John. The Loving Dominant. Masquerade, 1998. [1563336006]

Waugh, Evelyn. Brideshead Revisited. Little Brown, 1945. [0316926345]

Wertheimer, Neil, ed. Total Health for Men. Rodale Press, 1995. [0875964591]

Wiseman, Jay. SM 101: A Realistic Introduction. 2nd ed. Greenery, 1996. [0963976389]

Wodehouse, P.G. Life with Jeeves. Penguin, 1981. [0140059024]

Wright, Jeni and Eric Treuillé. Le Cordon Bleu Complete Cooking Techniques. Morrow, 1996. [0688152066]

Yenawine, Philip. Key Art Terms for Beginners. Abrams, 1995. [0810912252]

Zilbergeld, Bernie. The New Male Sexuality. Bantam, 1992. [0553562592]

Zraly, Kevin. Windows on the World Complete Wine Course. Dell, 1985. [0440596114]

Other Books from Greenery Press

BDSM/KINK

The Bullwhip Book
Andrew Conway $11.95

The Compleat Spanker
Lady Green $12.95

Erotic Tickling
Michael Moran $13.95

Family Jewels: A Guide to Male Genital Play and Torment
Hardy Haberman $12.95

Flogging
Joseph W. Bean $11.95

Intimate Invasions: The Ins and Outs of Erotic Enema Play
M.R. Strict $13.95

Jay Wiseman's Erotic Bondage Handbook
Jay Wiseman $16.95

The Loving Dominant
John Warren $16.95

Miss Abernathy's Concise Slave Training Manual
Christina Abernathy $12.95

The Mistress Manual: The Good Girl's Guide to Female Dominance
Mistress Lorelei $16.95

The New Bottoming Book
The New Topping Book
both by Dossie Easton & Janet W. Hardy $14.95

The Seductive Art of Japanese Bondage
Midori $27.95

The Sexually Dominant Woman: A Workbook for Nervous Beginners
Lady Green $11.95

SM 101: A Realistic Introduction
Jay Wiseman $24.95

Training With Miss Abernathy: A Workbook for Erotic Slaves and Their Owners
Christina Abernathy $13.95

GENERAL SEXUALITY

Big Big Love: A Sourcebook on Sex for People of Size and Those Who Love Them
Hanne Blank $15.95

The Bride Wore Black Leather... And He Looked Fabulous!: An Etiquette Guide for the Rest of Us
Andrew Campbell $11.95

The Ethical Slut: A Guide to Infinite Sexual Possibilities
Dossie Easton & Catherine A. Liszt $16.95

A Hand in the Bush: The Fine Art of Vaginal Fisting
Deborah Addington $13.95

Health Care Without Shame: A Handbook for the Sexually Diverse and Their Caregivers
Charles Moser, Ph.D., M.D. $11.95

The Lazy Crossdresser
Charles Anders $13.95

Look Into My Eyes: How to Use Hypnosis to Bring Out the Best in Your Sex Life
Peter Masters $16.95

Phone Sex: Oral Thrills and Aural Skills
Miranda Austin $15.95

Sex Disasters... And How to Survive Them
C. Moser, Ph.D., M.D. and J. Hardy $16.95

Tricks... To Please a Man
Tricks... To Please a Woman
both by Jay Wiseman $14.95

Turning Pro: A Guide to Sex Work for the Ambitious and the Intrigued
Magdalene Meretrix $16.95

When Someone You Love Is Kinky
Dossie Easton & Catherine A. Liszt $15.95

FICTION

The 43rd Mistress: A Sensual Odyssey
Grant Antrews $11.95

... But I Know What You Want: 25 Sex Tales for the Different
James Williams $13.95

Haughty Spirit
Sharon Green $11.95

Love, Sal: letters from a boy in The City
Sal Iacopelli, ill. Phil Foglio $13.95

Murder At Roissy
John Warren $15.95

The Warrior Within
The Warrior Enchained
both by Sharon Green $11.95

Please include $3 for first book and $1 for each additional book with your order to cover shipping and handling costs, plus $10 for overseas orders. VISA/MC accepted. Order from:

greenery press
3403 Piedmont Ave. #301, Oakland, CA 94611 toll-free 888/944-4434 www.greenerypress.com